Review & Reteach

Skills and Content Review
Grades 6, 7, & 8 Science

Needham, Massachusetts
Upper Saddle River, New Jersey
Glenview, Illinois

Prentice Hall

ISBN 0-13-064306-8

2 3 4 5 6 7 8 9 10   05 04 03 02

CONTENTS

CONTENTS (continued)

CONTENTS (continued)

CONTENTS (continued)

Welcome to
Review & Reteach: Skills and Content Review Grades 6, 7, & 8 Science

Part of the Prentice Hall Science Assessment System, *Skills and Content Review* serves as the companion to *Diagnose & Prescribe: Diagnostic Assessment*. *Diagnostic Assessment* is designed to help you identify content and topics that students may not fully understand. Once these content areas are identified, *Skills and Content Review* assists you in helping your students enhance their understanding of the concepts.

Within these pages you will find a review of science process skills, math skills, and content from life science, Earth science, and physical science. Also included is a complete middle grades science glossary. The book provides a convenient reference for you whenever you wish to revisit a topic or reteach a concept. It can serve as a guide for you to follow when reviewing content with your students. Plus, the pages can be photocopied and distributed to your class for use as review sheets.

The book is divided into sections, identified by black thumb tabs along the outside edge of the pages. The first section provides descriptions and examples of process skills that students need to acquire in order to be successful in the science classrooom.

Next is the content review section. Organized by subject area (life, Earth, and physical science), the content review pages cover the essential information associated with each topic in the Science Explorer middle grades curriculum.

Following the content review is the math skills section. Each skill is presented in a step-by-step process illustrating the skill. The skills covered are those that are especially important in science, such as using equations, calculating volume, and converting in the metric system.

The final component in the book is a middle grades glossary. Compiled from life science, Earth science, and physical science subject matter, the glossary contains more than 1,200 terms that students may find on standardized tests, as well as in the classroom and perhaps in their daily lives.

How to Use This Book

Once your students have worked through *Diagnostic Assessment* and you have recorded their results, you can identify areas that they may not fully understand. The *Diagnostic Assessment* book will then direct you to specific sections of this book, *Skills and Content Review,* where you will find material to help you address topics of particular concern. (Specific instructions on how to score and interpret the results, as well as a guide to how and where to find reteaching resources in the Science Explorer program, appear in *Diagnostic Assessment.*)

If, for instance, the results of the diagnostic test indicate that a student does not have an adequate understanding of plate tectonics, then you will be referred to the review of Topic 1: Inside Earth in the Earth science content review portion of this book. Once there, you will want to turn to the review of Chapter 1: Plate Tectonics, where you will find the main ideas presented in the chapter, as well as key terms related to the topic.

At this point, you can present an overview of the material to the class or provide the content of the review page to students for independent review. Or, you may wish to reteach the topic, to provide students with a more in-depth review and an opportunity to bolster their understanding.

Other valuable Science Explorer resources are also available when you are helping students refine their understanding of science. The **Guided Reading and Study Workbook** encourages active reading and provides students with various types of questions and exercises that relate directly to the curriculum. The **Teaching Resources with Color Transparencies, Unit Resources,** and **Color Transparencies** books offer support for both teacher and student. In them you'll find lesson plans and ideas on how to present each chapter to the class, as well as Review and Reinforce worksheets for your students. The transparencies review topics by graphical representation and give you the opportunity to work through an idea with the whole class at once.

Also, visit our Web site (**www.phschool.com**), where you will find activities and teaching resources for every chapter of the Prentice Hall Science Explorer textbooks. Be sure to check out **iText**, an online interactive version of the student editions that gives students self-assessment opportunities with instant feedback.

With your guidance and the Prentice Hall Assessment System for Middle Grades Science, your students will increase the depth and scope of their understanding of science concepts. Their confidence will increase. With more substantial understanding and confidence, students will find greater success in the science classroom as well as in other areas of their lives.

The Prentice Hall Science Explorer program is the foundation of the content reviewed in this book. If you find a need for a depth of review beyond what is presented in these pages, or a need to reteach a topic, you can return to the Science Explorer textbooks and easily find the corresponding material.

If you use the fifteen-book program, follow the first set of correlations below. If you use the Life, Earth, Physical (LEP) program, follow the second set.

The material in the content review section corresponds directly to the Science Explorer fifteen-book program. What is called a Topic in this book is the title of one of the fifteen books. The Topics match up with the books as follows:

Life Science Topic 1 = Science Explorer Book A
Life Science Topic 2 = Science Explorer Book B
Life Science Topic 3 = Science Explorer Book C
Life Science Topic 4 = Science Explorer Book D
Life Science Topic 5 = Science Explorer Book E

Earth Science Topic 1 = Science Explorer Book F
Earth Science Topic 2 = Science Explorer Book G
Earth Science Topic 3 = Science Explorer Book H
Earth Science Topic 4 = Science Explorer Book I
Earth Science Topic 5 = Science Explorer Book J

Physical Science Topic 1 = Science Explorer Book K
Physical Science Topic 2 = Science Explorer Book L
Physical Science Topic 3 = Science Explorer Book M
Physical Science Topic 4 = Science Explorer Book N
Physical Science Topic 5 = Science Explorer Book O

The content covered herein can be found in the Science Explorer Life, Earth, and Physical (LEP) program, in the following locations:

Life Science Topic 1
    Chapter 1: LEP Life Science Chapter 1, Chapter 6
    Chapter 2: LEP Life Science Chapter 6
    Chapter 3: LEP Life Science Chapter 7
    Chapter 4: LEP Life Science Chapter 8
    Chapter 5: LEP Life Science Chapter 8, Chapter 9

Life Science Topic 2
    Chapter 1: LEP Life Science Chapter 10
    Chapter 2: LEP Life Science Chapter 11
    Chapter 3: LEP Life Science Chapter 12
    Chapter 4: LEP Life Science Chapter 13
    Chapter 5: LEP Life Science Chapter 11, Chapter 14

Life Science Topic 3
    Chapter 1: LEP Life Science Chapter 1, Chapter 2
    Chapter 2: LEP Life Science Chapter 2
    Chapter 3: LEP Life Science Chapter 3
    Chapter 4: LEP Life Science Chapter 4
    Chapter 5: LEP Life Science Chapter 5

Life Science Topic 4
    Chapter 1: LEP Life Science Chapter 15
    Chapter 2: LEP Life Science Chapter 15
    Chapter 3: LEP Life Science Chapter 16
    Chapter 4: LEP Life Science Chapter 17
    Chapter 5: LEP Life Science Chapter 18
    Chapter 6: LEP Life Science Chapter 19
    Chapter 7: LEP Life Science Chapter 20
    Chapter 8: LEP Life Science Chapter 21

Life Science Topic 5
    Chapter 1: LEP Life Science Chapter 22
    Chapter 2: LEP Life Science Chapter 23
    Chapter 3: LEP Life Science Chapter 24
    Chapter 4: LEP Earth Science Chapter 7
    Chapter 5: LEP Earth Science Chapter 12,
        Chapter 15, Chapter 18
    Chapter 6: LEP Earth Science Chapter 10

Earth Science Topic 1
    Chapter 1: LEP Earth Science Chapter 4
    Chapter 2: LEP Earth Science Chapter 5
    Chapter 3: LEP Earth Science Chapter 6
    Chapter 4: LEP Earth Science Chapter 2
    Chapter 5: LEP Earth Science Chapter 3

Earth Science Topic 2
    Chapter 1: LEP Earth Science Chapter 1
    Chapter 2: LEP Earth Science Chapter 7
    Chapter 3: LEP Earth Science Chapter 8
    Chapter 4: LEP Earth Science Chapter 9

Earth Science Topic 3
    Chapter 1: LEP Earth Science Chapter 11
    Chapter 2: LEP Earth Science Chapter 11
    Chapter 3: LEP Earth Science Chapter 12
    Chapter 4: LEP Earth Science Chapter 13
    Chapter 5: LEP Earth Science Chapter 14

Earth Science Topic 4
    Chapter 1: LEP Earth Science Chapter 15
    Chapter 2: LEP Earth Science Chapter 16
    Chapter 3: LEP Earth Science Chapter 17
    Chapter 4: LEP Earth Science Chapter 18

Earth Science Topic 5
    Chapter 1: LEP Earth Science Chapter 19
    Chapter 2: LEP Earth Science Chapter 20
    Chapter 3: LEP Earth Science Chapter 21

Physical Science Topic 1
    Chapter 1: LEP Physical Science Chapter 1
    Chapter 2: LEP Physical Science Chapter 2
    Chapter 3: LEP Physical Science Chapter 3
    Chapter 4: LEP Physical Science Chapter 7

Physical Science Topic 2
    Chapter 1: LEP Physical Science Chapter 5
    Chapter 2: LEP Physical Science Chapter 3,
        Chapter 4
    Chapter 3: LEP Physical Science Chapter 6
    Chapter 4: LEP Physical Science Chapter 8

Physical Science Topic 3
    Chapter 1: LEP Physical Science Chapter 9
    Chapter 2: LEP Physical Science Chapter 10
    Chapter 3: LEP Physical Science Chapter 11
    Chapter 4: LEP Physical Science Chapter 12
    Chapter 5: LEP Physical Science Chapter 13
    Chapter 6: LEP Physical Science Chapter 14

Physical Science Topic 4
    Chapter 1: LEP Physical Science Chapter 19
    Chapter 2: LEP Physical Science Chapter 20
    Chapter 3: LEP Physical Science Chapter 21
    Chapter 4: LEP Physical Science Chapter 22

Physical Science Topic 5
    Chapter 1: LEP Physical Science Chapter 15
    Chapter 2: LEP Physical Science Chapter 16
    Chapter 3: LEP Physical Science Chapter 17
    Chapter 4: LEP Physical Science Chapter 18

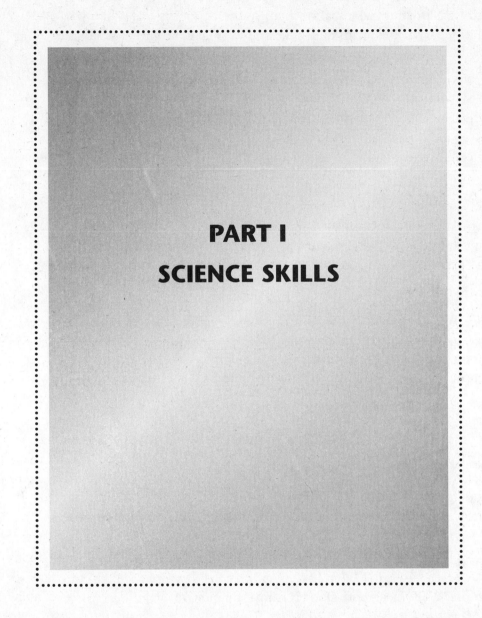

PART I
SCIENCE SKILLS

Observing

The first day of school is an exciting time. You find out who your teachers are, who else is in your classes, and where your classrooms are. When you look around to see what the room looks like and who is there, you are making observations.

Observing is using one or more of your senses—sight, hearing, smell, taste, and touch—to gather information about the world. For example, seeing a green chalkboard, hearing a bell ring, smelling smoke, tasting a sour lemon, and feeling a smooth desktop are observations. Information gathered from observations is called evidence, or data. Making and recording observations is the most basic skill in science.

When you make observations in science, you want them to be accurate and objective. An accurate observation is an exact report of what your senses tell you. An objective observation avoids opinions, or bias, based on specific points of view.

> **Example 1:** Sixteen students were present for roll call, and five other students arrived afterward. (accurate and objective)

> **Example 2:** Half the students were late. (not accurate)

> **Example 3:** The friendliest people were there first. (not objective)

Observations can be either qualitative or quantitative. Qualitative observations are descriptions that do not use numbers. For example, if you report colors, odors, tastes, textures, or sounds, you are making qualitative observations. Quantitative observations, on the other hand, do include numbers. If you count objects or measure them with standard units, you are making quantitative observations. Quantitative observations are often made using tools.

> **Example 4:** The classroom walls are yellow. (qualitative)

> **Example 5:** The classroom floor is shiny. (qualitative)

> **Example 6:** There are 21 students in the room. (quantitative)

> **Example 7:** The chalkboard is 1 m high and 2 m wide. (quantitative)

Observing (continued)

In science, observations are usually followed by attempted explanations, or inferences. When scientists make inferences from observations, however, they keep the two processes separate. That's because although an accurate observation is considered to be factual evidence, the inferences may not be correct. When you make and record your observations, write down just what your senses perceive.

Example 8: There's an empty aquarium tank in the classroom. (observation)

Example 9: The tank is 50 cm long, 30 cm wide, and 18 cm deep. (observation)

Example 10: The tank once contained live fish. (an inference, not an observation)

Example 11: The tank is waterproof. (an inference, not an observation)

Tips for Making Observations

◆ Use the senses of sight, hearing, touch, and smell to make qualitative observations. Important: For safety's sake, do not taste any unknown substances.

◆ Review your observations to make sure they are accurate and objective.

◆ Whenever possible, count or use instruments to make quantitative observations. Make sure you include the unit that identifies each measurement, such as a mass measurement of 5 grams or a distance measurement of 15 meters.

◆ If no tools are available to make measurements, try to estimate common quantities by referring to known standards. For example, you might state that an object is about as long as a new pencil, or has the mass of a paper clip.

◆ Check your observations to be sure that they are statements about information gained through your senses, not explanations of what you observed.

Inferring

Have you ever come home, smelled fish cooking, and thought, "We're having fish for dinner"? You made an observation with your sense of smell and used past experience to conclude what your next meal would be. Such a conclusion is called an inference.

Making an inference, or **inferring,** is explaining or interpreting an observation or statement. Inferences can be reasonable (logical) or unreasonable. A reasonable inference is one that makes sense, given what a person knows about the topic. One way to make an unreasonable inference is to conclude too much from the evidence.

For example, suppose you are on a photo safari in Africa. In a region bordering some small farms, you see some domestic cattle sharing space with some wild antelope. Some people in your group make the following observations and inferences.

Observation: The cattle and the antelope are standing quietly together.

Inference 1: The cattle and antelope do not attack each other. (reasonable)

Inference 2: None of the animals in this region attack each other. (unreasonable, because you have no evidence about any other animals)

Observation: Some of the cattle are eating grass.

Inference 3: The grass is food for the cattle and antelope. (reasonable)

Inference 4: Most of the grass in this area is eaten by the cattle. (unreasonable, because you have no evidence about the amounts eaten)

Skills and Content Review

Often you can make more than one logical inference from the same observation. Remember: A logical inference must make sense in terms of everything else you know.

Observation: The antelope are looking around.

Inference 5: The antelope are watching for predators. (reasonable)

Inference 6: The antelope are watching for potential mates. (reasonable)

Inference 7: The antelope heard you coming through the brush. (reasonable)

When you first make a logical inference, you may not know whether it's true or false. What's important is to make sure the inference is reasonable and based on accurate evidence. Then you can obtain additional evidence to find out whether the inference is correct. For example, if you talked to the farmers who own the cattle in the illustration, you would find out that the cattle eat grass, but the antelope do not.

▶ Tips for Making Inferences

◆ Base your inference on accurate qualitative or quantitative observations.

◆ Combine your observations with knowledge or experience to make an inference.

◆ Try to make more than one logical inference from the same observation.

◆ Evaluate the inferences. Decide what new information you need to show whether your inferences are true. If necessary, gather more information.

◆ Be prepared to modify, reject, or revise your inferences.

Predicting

If a family moves into your neighborhood, your new neighbors may ask you questions like these: How many games will the school soccer team win? Will the math teacher give hard quizzes? How long will it take to get to the library? Questions like these ask you to make predictions. Predictions are a normal part of everyday life, but they also have an important place in science.

Predicting is making an inference about a future event based on current evidence or past experience. One way to make a prediction is to look for a pattern. For instance, depending on how many games your soccer team won last year, and whether the same players are on the team, you might make one of the predictions below. Notice that these predictions differ in how specific they are.

> **Example 1:** Our team will lose a lot of games this year.
> (general)
>
> **Example 2:** Our team will win about half of its games this year.
> (somewhat specific)
>
> **Example 3:** Our team will win at least six games, but it will lose to
> Central Community School. (quite specific)

When you make a prediction in science, try to make it as specific as you can. Don't just guess. Consider all the experiences and knowledge you have about the topic. Also examine any new information you can obtain, by analyzing data tables and graphs, for example. Then make a reasonable inference based on all that information.

You may have made a logical prediction that did not come true. As a result, you probably know that predictions are not always correct. Because a prediction is an inference—an explanation or an interpretation of observations—it may not turn out to be true.

In science, predictions are usually tested. Some predictions can be tested by making observations. For instance, if someone predicts the times for sunrise and sunset over the next 30 days, you can test those predictions by using an accurate watch to time the events each day. On other occasions, carefully planned tests may be needed. For instance, suppose someone makes this prediction:

> "This new medicine will prevent the common cold."

The only way to test such a statement would be to carry out a controlled experiment. Regardless of whether tests show a scientific prediction to be true or false, making and testing predictions is a proven way of increasing people's understanding of the natural world.

Skills and Content Review

▶ Tips for Making Predictions

◆ When you make a prediction about an event, don't just guess. Examine all the evidence that's available to you, including information in data tables and graphs. Also recall what you know about the topic.

◆ Look for a pattern in the evidence or in what you know. Consider how that pattern applies to the event you're predicting.

◆ If you don't have enough information, try to find out more about the event or about similar events.

◆ Don't be discouraged if your prediction turns out to be false. Remember that the purpose of making a prediction in science is to learn about the natural world. Always ask yourself, "What did I learn from making and testing this prediction?" Your early incorrect predictions may lead you to new questions and new predictions that will increase your knowledge.

Classifying

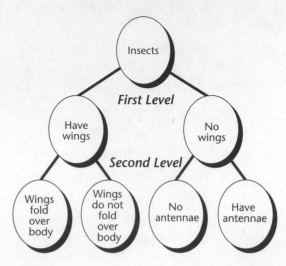

Can you imagine shopping for a CD in a store that kept its recordings in a single, huge pile? Chances are you'd take your business to a place that classified CDs into groups, such as rock, rap, country, and other categories.

Classifying is organizing objects and events into groups according to a system, or organizing idea. The most simple type of classification system uses two groups, one that has a certain property and another that does not. Other systems may begin with three or more groups.

> **Example 1:** Plants With Wood; Plants Without Wood (simplest system using two groups)

> **Example 2:** Locations at Sea Level, Locations Above Sea Level; Locations Below Sea Level (three groups based on one idea)

Many classification systems, like the one in the diagram above, have more than one level. Each of the first-level groups in the system is further classified into smaller categories based on new organizing ideas.

In science, objects and processes can be classified in different ways. Scientists choose the system that best suits their purpose. They may classify to organize objects, such as the chemicals stored in a laboratory. They also classify to help simplify and make sense of the natural world. Good classification systems make finding information easier. They also help to clarify the relationships among the things being classified.

▶ ## Tips for Classifying

- ◆ Carefully observe the group of objects to be classified. Identify similarities and differences among the objects.

- ◆ Choose a characteristic that some of the objects share. Use this characteristic as the organizing idea, and place the objects into groups.

- ◆ Examine the groups and decide if they can be further classified. Each round of further classification may need a different organizing idea.

Making Models

You may know someone who builds model trains, ships, or dollhouses as a hobby. In some occupations, people use models to plan complex objects, such as buildings. Models also play a role in science. Scientific **models** are pictures, diagrams, or other representations of objects or processes. Models may be created on paper or a computer, or may be made of wood, metal, plastic, or other materials. Making scientific models helps people understand natural objects and processes.

There are two main types of models. Physical models, such as model skeletons, usually look like the object or process being modeled. Mental models, such as mathematical equations, represent ideas about objects or processes that often cannot be observed directly. For example, for centuries, most people thought that the world was flat. A few scientists developed the hypothesis that Earth is shaped like a ball. They could then make a mathematical model that included the diameter of Earth and use an equation to find Earth's surface area.

Physical models can be either two-dimensional (flat), such as a map, or three-dimensional (with depth), such as a globe. Scientists often use physical models to represent things that are very large (such as the solar system), very small (atoms), or not easily visible (bacteria). Some models are drawn "to scale." That means that the measurements of the model are in proportion to the actual object. For example, a model may be 100 times larger than or $\frac{1}{10}$ the size of the actual object.

▶ Tips for Making Models

- ◆ Identify the purpose of the model and the type of model to be used (physical or mental, two-dimensional or three-dimensional).

- ◆ If you are modeling a process, try to think through the entire process and identify its steps in order.

- ◆ If you are making a physical model, determine what materials you will use.

- ◆ Decide whether the model will be larger than, smaller than, or the same size as the real object. Will it be made to scale? If so, what scale?

- ◆ Make a plan before you begin making the model. Use a pencil to list or draw your ideas, and have an eraser handy so you can revise your plan easily. Be prepared to explain any important differences between the model and the real thing.

Communicating

You have probably waved to a friend from a distance, written someone a note, and had more conversations than you can count. Whenever you send messages to, or receive messages from, another person, you are **communicating.** Since you've been communicating your whole life, you may wonder what else you need to learn about the topic.

Now you are learning how scientists communicate. In science, observations and experiments should be reproducible. That means that any scientist should understand and be able to repeat the work of another scientist. To make such repetition possible, scientists follow certain rules when they communicate.

◆ The descriptions of all procedures must be understandable and complete. Someone else should be able to repeat the entire procedure step by step.

◆ Observations, or evidence, must be recorded accurately and in total. Researchers who observe unexpected or puzzling results must report these results.

◆ The observations should be discussed separately from the inferences, or explanations of the observations. Other scientists may make different inferences from the same observations.

◆ Scientific work should be objective—free from bias. In science, being free from bias means considering all reasonable explanations instead of just trying to prove a specific idea.

As you study science, you'll have many opportunities to communicate, sometimes orally and other times in writing.

Oral Communication   Scientific communication may occur orally. Scientists frequently share their ideas in person and by telephone. You too will have opportunities to talk about science topics when you work in small groups or make presentations to your class. Besides observing the rules described in the previous section, try to remember the following:

◆ Your ideas may be new to your audience. Watch people's faces to see if they understand you. You may need to repeat an idea or explain it in a different way.

◆ Consider using visuals or models. In small groups, you could make simple sketches. For class presentations, you could prepare larger, more complex displays.

Written Communication   Most scientific communication occurs through the written or printed word. New research is nearly always reported in printed form, usually in science journals. Similarly, you may need to write up the procedures and results of your experiments in a lab report. Lab reports usually contain the following sections, in this order:

(1) problem or question

(2) hypothesis

(3) list of materials

(4) procedure

(5) observations, often organized in data tables

(6) analysis, including any calculations and graphs

(7) conclusions

Sometimes lab reports end with additional questions suggested by the conclusion, or ideas for additional experiments.

▶ Tips for Communicating in Science

◆ Describe your observations honestly and completely. Write what you actually observe, not what you expected to observe or hoped would happen.

◆ Record your observations as clearly and efficiently as possible, using data tables, for example. If you make data tables afterward, always create those data tables from your original notes. Don't rewrite your notes to make them sound better.

◆ Keep a written record of your procedures, including any changes you make as you work. Always be prepared to communicate your procedures to others.

◆ Present your observations and your inferences separately.

◆ Use graphs and diagrams when they will help interpret your data. If you carry out calculations, show the formula or describe the mathematical operations you performed.

◆ Follow any rules or guidelines that apply to the specific type of communication (for example, lab reports, science fair presentations, and class projects).

◆ If you use information from other people's work, keep a record of those references and the information you obtained from them. Be prepared to provide the names of your sources.

Measuring

If you enjoy sports, you know how exciting it is when an athlete swims faster, runs longer, or hits a ball farther than other competitors. You also know that people aren't satisfied with descriptions like "faster" or "longer." They want exact statistics showing just how fast an athlete ran and how great the margin of victory was. Measurements can help make sports more fun.

Common SI Units		
Property	**Basic Unit**	**Symbol**
Length	meter	m
Liquid volume	liter	L
Mass	gram	g
Temperature	degree Celsius	°C

Measurements are also important in science because they provide important specific information and help observers avoid bias. **Measuring** is comparing an object or process to a standard. Scientists use a common set of standards, called the International System of Units. This system is often abbreviated as SI (for its French name, *Système International d'Unités*). The table above lists the basic units for four common properties.

The basic unit of length is the meter. For a property such as length, researchers often need to measure amounts that are much smaller or much larger than the basic unit. In the SI system, the smaller or larger units are based on multiples of 10. For example, notice that the meter below is divided into 10 main sections, called decimeters. That means that a decimeter is $\frac{1}{10}$ (or 0.1) of a meter.

Each decimeter is then divided into ten sections, called centimeters. A centimeter is $\frac{1}{100}$ (or 0.01) of a meter. A millimeter is $\frac{1}{1,000}$ (or 0.001) of a meter.

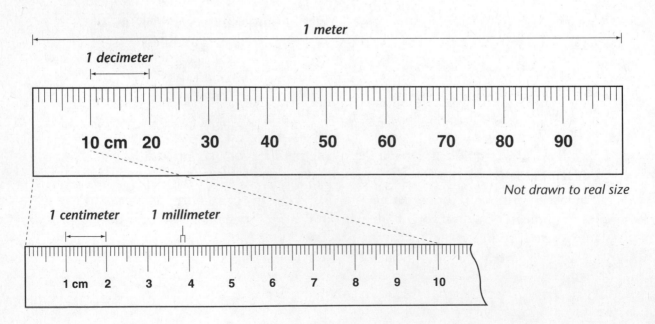

Not drawn to real size

Skills and Content Review

The same prefixes that are used for naming smaller and larger units of length are also used for naming different size units of volume and mass. Look at the chart below to see the meaning of some common prefixes.

Common SI Prefixes			
Prefix	**Symbol**	**Meaning**	**Example**
kilo-	k	1,000	kilometer (km)
hecto-	h	100	hectometer (hm)
deka-	da	10	dekameter (dam)
deci-	d	$0.1 \left(\frac{1}{10}\right)$	decimeter (dm)
centi-	c	$0.01 \left(\frac{1}{100}\right)$	centimeter (cm)
milli-	m	$0.001 \left(\frac{1}{1,000}\right)$	millimeter (mm)

Tips for Making Measurements

◆ Know the purpose of your measurement. Choose the most suitable size unit (for example, centimeters for a book or meters for the classroom floor).

◆ Know how your measuring tool works (for example, what main units it measures and what the smaller units mean).

◆ Always label your measurements. If you perform any math operations, such as adding or subtracting measurements, always label the resulting numbers properly.

◆ Determine whether you will need one, two, or a series of measurements. Figure out whether you will have to perform any math operations. For example, if you need to find how much the temperature of a liquid increased, you will need to subtract the original temperature from the final temperature.

◆ Know any special rules that apply. For example, read the water level in a graduated cylinder at eye level and at the lowest point of the curved surface.

Calculating

Scientists must often solve problems that involve very large or very small numbers. For example, astronomers study galaxies with millions of stars that are at great distances from Earth. Microbiologists measure organisms or parts of organisms that can be seen only with the most powerful microscopes. Physicists investigate particles that are even smaller. Making calculations is important in the work of these and other scientists. **Calculating** is a process in which a person uses mathematical operations such as addition, subtraction, multiplication, and division to manipulate numbers and symbols.

One important type of calculation you will need to make is converting units of measure. That means changing one unit of measure into a different unit of measure that represents the same amount. For example, if you have 220 dimes, how many dollars do you have? Because you know there are 10 dimes in a dollar, you can easily convert the dimes to dollars with this procedure.

$$220 \text{ dimes} \times \frac{\$1}{10 \text{ dimes}} = \frac{\$220}{10} = \$22$$

In science, you will need to convert between SI, or metric, units. Like the dollar system, the SI system is a decimal system. The table below lists some common metric conversions.

Common Metric Conversions	
Length	1 km = 1,000 m
	1 m = 100 cm
	1 m = 1,000 mm
	1 cm = 10 mm
Liquid volume	1 L = 1,000 mL
Mass	1 kg = 1,000 g

For example, suppose you need to convert 117 millimeters into centimeters. One way to make the conversion is to follow the procedure that was just used to convert dimes to dollars:

$$117 \text{ millimeters} \times \frac{1 \text{ centimeter}}{10 \text{ millimeters}} = \frac{117}{10} \text{ centimeters} = 11.7 \text{ centimeters}$$

Tips for Calculating

Follow these steps when converting between units.

1. Begin by writing down the measurement you want to convert on the left side of the equation. Suppose you want to convert 1.6 liters to milliliters. Write:

    1.6 liters ×

2. Write a conversion factor that represents the relationship between the two units you are converting: 1 liter = 1,000 milliliters. Writing this conversion factor as the correct fraction is an important step.

    $$1.6 \text{ liters} \times \frac{1,000 \text{ milliliters}}{1 \text{ liter}}$$

    Make sure you place the units you are starting with—liters, in this example—in the denominator. In the next step, you will see why that is important.

3. Multiply the measurement you want to convert by the conversion factor. When you multiply these two terms, the units in the first measurement will cancel out with the units in the denominator. The result will be a fraction.

    $$1.6 \cancel{\text{ liters}} \times \frac{1,000 \text{ milliliters}}{1 \cancel{\text{ liter}}} = \frac{1,600.0}{1} \text{ milliliters}$$

4. Divide the numerator of the fraction by the denominator. Your answer will be in the units you are trying to find.

    $$1.6 \cancel{\text{ liters}} \times \frac{1,000 \text{ milliliters}}{1 \cancel{\text{ liter}}} = \frac{1,600.0}{1} \text{ milliliters} = 1,600 \text{ milliliters}$$

Designing Experiments

Have you ever timed two different routes to school or compared two kinds of shampoo? If so, you have performed a simple experiment. You probably didn't plan your experiment on paper before you carried it out. Scientists, however, design experiments carefully before actually performing them. **Designing an experiment** is making an organized plan to test a hypothesis. An experimental design usually follows a definite pattern. When you design experiments according to this pattern, you will use many individual science skills. Some of these skills are described briefly below.

Pose a Question

Scientists design experiments to answer questions or solve problems. For example, suppose you've heard people say that adding sugar to the water in a vase of flowers keeps the flowers fresh. You wonder whether that statement is true. To find out, you will perform an experiment. You write the topic to be investigated in the form of a scientific question: "Does adding sugar to water keep flowers fresh?"

Develop a Hypothesis

A hypothesis is a possible explanation for a set of observations or answer to a scientific question. For example, you could write *Adding sugar to the water in a vase keeps the flowers fresh longer.*

Plan the Procedure

The procedure describes what you plan to do and identifies the data you plan to collect. Begin by identifying the manipulated variable—the factor you will purposely change—and the responding variable—the factor you predict will change as a result of the manipulated variable. Here, the manipulated variable is the presence or absence of sugar in the water. The responding variable is the length of time that the flowers remain fresh. The procedure is a step-by-step description of how you will change the manipulated variable and observe the effects upon the responding variable. Preparing a data table for recording your observations is a key part of planning the procedure.

Before you begin carrying out the procedure, you must also identify the materials you will need. Write a list of those materials and then continue making your plan. When your plan is complete, revise the materials list, if necessary.

© Pearson Education, Inc.

Skills and Content Review

Controlling Variables To be sure that your results are caused only by changes in the manipulated variable, you need to control all other variables that might affect your experiment. Controlling variables means keeping conditions the same. For example, you would keep all the flowers at the same temperature. Other variables you would control include the type and size of the containers, the number of flowers in each container, and the amount of light they receive.

Writing Operational Definitions To enable anyone to repeat and test your experiment, you must write an operational definition for any key term that does not have a single, clear meaning. For example, you could define "remaining fresh" as "flowers keeping their petals." That definition tells anyone how to measure the responding variable.

Interpret the Data

During the experiment, you record all your observations. These observations are your data. Interpreting the data means explaining that data. You may make simple comparisons or look for trends or patterns. For example, if flowers in both groups kept the same number of petals, both groups of flowers stayed fresh the same length of time.

Draw Conclusions

After you interpret the data, you need to compare that interpretation with your hypothesis and decide whether the hypothesis was true or false. This step is called drawing a conclusion. This step may conclude a scientist's investigation, or it may lead the scientist to raise new questions and design new experiments.

Why isn't my radio working? What's the most popular radio program? How does a radio work? What's the best kind of music? These are different kinds of questions you might ask. Some of them concern physical objects. Others are based on values or opinions—what people believe is right or wrong, or beautiful or ugly.

Questions are an essential part of science. But scientific questions are limited to the natural world—to material objects and energy changes you can observe directly or with scientific tools. The objects may be either living or nonliving things. The energy changes may be easy to observe, such as the sound of thunder overhead, or more difficult, such as the light coming from a distant star. What makes a question scientific is that it can be answered by observations, or evidence.

Scientists may start with a broad question such as "Why do people get colds?" Next, they break the question down into smaller questions: Can you catch a cold from someone else? Is there a relationship between getting chills and catching a cold? They state the final question in a way that can be answered by investigation or experiment. A good scientific question is "Does getting chilled cause colds?"

Narrowing down a question often helps researchers plan an investigation and gather evidence to answer the question. For example, to determine whether chills cause colds, a scientist could ask volunteers to undergo low temperatures that produce chills. If few or no volunteers catch colds, the scientist has obtained evidence to answer the question.

▶ Tips for Posing Questions

- Begin by listing several questions on a topic about the natural world.
- Try to eliminate questions that cannot be answered by gathering evidence.
- Break broad questions into questions that can be investigated one at a time.
- Word questions in a way that allows them to be answered by an investigation or experiment. Here are some good ways to begin scientific questions: "What is the relationship between . . . ?" "What factors cause . . . ?" "What is the effect of . . . ?" Be sure that the question identifies a relationship or factor you can investigate.

Developing Hypotheses

Suppose you and your neighbor are growing tomatoes. One day you notice that your neighbor's plants are much bigger than yours. What's causing the difference? How can you get your plants to grow as big as your neighbor's?

The question you asked about the tomato plants could lead you to develop a hypothesis. A **hypothesis** (plural: *hypotheses*) is a possible explanation for a set of observations or answer to a scientific question. Hypotheses are based on a person's observations and previous knowledge or experience.

In science, hypotheses must be testable. That means that researchers should be able to carry out an investigation and obtain evidence that shows whether the hypothesis is true or false.

Read the following examples. Notice which of the hypotheses is testable.

Example 1: Fertilizer makes plants grow bigger. (testable)

Example 2: With luck, plants will grow bigger. (not testable, because you can't control or measure "luck")

Scientists use a hypothesis to write a prediction. Sometimes the prediction is worded as an *If . . . then . . .* statement. For example, the hypothesis in Example 1 can lead to the following prediction: If I give my plants fertilizer, then they will grow big. The prediction is a rough outline of an experiment that can be performed to test the hypothesis.

▶ Tips for Developing Hypotheses

- ◆ Ideas for hypotheses often result from problems that have been identified or questions that have been raised. To help develop ideas for a hypothesis, write down several questions about the topic. Try to narrow the questions to one that can be investigated scientifically. Then write the hypothesis.

- ◆ Make sure the hypothesis is an explanation that is based on observation, previous knowledge, or experience.

- ◆ Make sure the hypothesis can be tested through an investigation.

- ◆ Use the hypothesis to write a prediction.

Controlling Variables

Suppose that you are planning to try out for the track team. To make the team, you need to increase your speed. You wonder whether to eat a new cereal being advertised for athletes. You could eat the cereal every morning for a month, then run a timed race. If your new time was faster than your previous time, would the cereal be the cause? Based on your test, there'd be no way to know! Too many factors could explain your improved speed. The only way to be sure whether a particular variable causes a specific result is to conduct a controlled experiment.

Every experiment involves several variables, or factors that can change. For example, consider this question: Will houseplants grow faster if you make the room warmer? To answer this question, you decide to grow plants at different temperatures. The variable that you purposely change and test—the temperature of the room—is called the **manipulated variable.** The factor that may change as a result of the manipulated variable—how fast the plants grow—is called the **responding variable.**

An experimental plan is not complete unless the experimenter controls the variables. **Controlling variables** means keeping all conditions the same except for the manipulated variable. In an experiment on temperature and plant growth, for example, you have to control any other variables that might affect the growth rate. Such variables include the size of the container, the type of soil, the amount of water, the amount of light, and the use of fertilizer. In addition, you would need to use identical plants in the experiment.

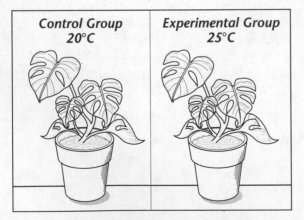

**Control Group
20°C**

**Experimental Group
25°C**

*Same kind of plant
Identical containers
Same type and amount of soil
Same type and amount of fertilizer
Same amount of water
Same lighting*

When all these variables are controlled, you can logically conclude that the differences in your results are due to changes in the manipulated variable.

How to Identify the Control Group In a controlled experiment, scientists usually study groups of living or nonliving things instead of comparing just two individual things. The groups that are being studied are called the experimental group and the control group. The experimental group is the group whose conditions are being changed. In the example on the previous page, the plants being grown at the warmer temperature of 25°C make up the experimental group. The control group, or the control, is the group whose conditions are *not* being changed. In the example, the plants grown at the usual temperature of 20°C make up the control group.

The purpose of the control group is to serve as a standard of comparison. For example, if the plants in the control group grew an average of 1 centimeter after 3 weeks, you could compare whether the plants in the experimental group grew the same amount, or grew more than or less than 1 centimeter.

▶ Tips for Controlling Variables

◆ Start by describing the question or process being investigated. Then identify the manipulated variable and the responding variable in the investigation. Predict the kinds of results you might observe in the responding variable.

◆ Create a list of all of the other variables that might affect the responding variable.

◆ Consider whether you have forgotten any of the most common types of variables: time, temperature, length, width, height, mass, volume, number, and the kinds of substances being used in the experiment.

◆ Determine whether or not one of the objects or groups of objects will serve as the control.

Forming Operational Definitions

Suppose that your class and another class work together on an experiment. You're trying to determine what kinds of balls roll the fastest. When the experiment is finished, you all want to compare your data, so you must all perform the experiment in the same way. That means that each time a team of students repeats the experiment, they have to use the same materials and procedure as every other team. They must also make their measurements in an identical manner.

Scientists also repeat investigations—their own and those of other researchers—to be sure that specific data are reliable. To make such repetition possible, scientists use operational definitions. An **operational definition** is a statement that describes how a particular variable is to be measured, or how an object or condition is to be recognized. Operational definitions tell you what to do or what to observe. (The word "operational" means "describing what to do.") Operational definitions need to be clear and precise so that a researcher knows exactly what to observe or measure.

In the experiment described above, the two classes could agree on a common procedure: Set up a ramp exactly 10 centimeters high and 2 meters long, and use tape to make a "finish line" at the bottom of the ramp. Make a series of tests by letting two different balls roll down the ramp at the same time. By using the following definition, the classes would eventually determine which ball rolls the fastest.

Example 1: Operational definition: The fastest ball is the one that crosses the finish line before all the other balls.

When you read or write an operational definition, ask yourself, "Does this definition describe what to do or what to observe?" In the example just given, the student teams would be able to use the procedure and the definition to compare their results. Here are some other examples of operational definitions.

Example 2: Lemon juice, vinegar, and certain other substances are acids. To find out whether a substance is an acid, place a drop of the substance on blue litmus paper. Operational definition: Substances that cause the litmus paper to turn pink are acids.

Example 3: To measure a person's pulse, place your index and middle fingers lightly on the inside of the person's wrist and find the beating artery. Operational definition: The pulse is the number of beats counted in 1 minute.

Example 4: You have to classify vertebrates as fish, amphibians, reptiles, birds, or mammals. Operational definition: A bird is an animal that has two feet, a pair of wings, and feathers.

Example 5: You have to determine the relative ages of layers of sedimentary rock. Operational definition: In sedimentary rock that has not been disturbed, the oldest rock is the bottom layer area, and the youngest rock is the top layer.

Often, it is possible to write more than one operational definition for a variable. For example, the speed of a moving object can be measured in many ways, such as with timed photographs, speedometers, or radar guns. When you write an operational definition, choose a procedure that makes sense for the investigation you're carrying out. Ask yourself: "Will the measurements I obtain with this definition give me data that help me test my hypothesis or answer my question?" If the answer is no, you need to rethink and revise your definition.

▶ Tips for Forming Operational Definitions

◆ Look over the written plan for carrying out an investigation, or write up a plan.

◆ Identify and list any variables or terms that do not have a single, clear, obvious meaning.

◆ If there are several reasonable ways to make an observation or to perform an action, choose one that suits the purpose of the investigation.

◆ Write a clear, complete definition of what the researcher should do or measure. Check your definition by asking yourself, "Will this definition tell another person what to observe or how to measure?" If necessary, revise your definition before starting your investigation.

Interpreting Data

Suppose your class is planning a party. You don't have lots of money to spend, so you're looking for bargains as you buy the food, drinks, and decorations. For example, you can buy soft drinks in separate cans, in packs of six cans, or in one-liter bottles. Some stores are having sales, and you also have a few money-saving coupons. To figure out the best price, you would first have to decide how many soft drinks you need, list all the price information you have, and then compare the various choices. That's similar to what you do when you analyze data in a science investigation.

During a science investigation, you make observations and take measurements that are called **data.** For example, you might observe color changes in a liquid or measure the temperature of objects left out in a sunny spot. After you collect your data, you need to interpret—or find meaning in—the data by looking for patterns or trends.

Suppose that scientists recorded the temperature at a specific location on Earth's surface. After that, they drilled below the surface to collect temperatures at different depths. The results of their work are shown in the table below.

Depth (km)	Temperature (°C)
0	15
1	52
2	88
3	120
4	151
5	179
6	206
7	232
8	257

By looking at the table, you can see that the deeper the location of the measurement, the higher the temperature. But it's hard to find any more details about that trend by just examining the table. So you decide to graph the data.

You could use the data to create a graph like this one. You could then interpret the graph and make inferences like the ones that follow.

Example 1: The deeper the location of the temperature reading beneath Earth's surface, the hotter the temperature is.

Example 2: For every additional kilometer of depth, the temperature increases about 30 Celsius degrees.

Example 3: The temperature at a depth of 3.5 km would be about 135°C.

To determine whether your interpretation of the data is logical, you compare it with what you already know. You know that lava from inside Earth sometimes erupts from volcanoes, and that lava is extremely hot. You decide your interpretation of the data makes sense.

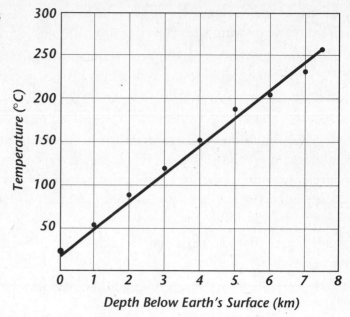

Depth Below Earth's Surface (km)

▶ Tips for Interpreting Data

◆ Organize the data into a table or arrange the data in a specific order, such as largest to smallest. If applicable, make calculations such as adding, subtracting, or finding averages.

◆ Make a graph of the data.

◆ Look for trends or patterns in the data or graph.

◆ Make one or more inferences from the data. Then compare the inferences with what you already know about the topic.

◆ If your inferences seem to contradict what you know, review your work to see whether you made any errors or need to examine the data again.

Drawing Conclusions

Suppose that you have a portable radio with headphones. One day you turn the radio on, but you don't hear your favorite station. You try other stations and still get no sound. You think that the batteries must be dead, so you put in new ones. Still there is no sound. You try replacing your headphones with ones from your sister's radio. Your favorite music is back! You draw the conclusion that there was something wrong with your headphones.

In everyday language, the word "conclusion" means an explanation or interpretation of an observation or a statement. In science, the word "conclusion" usually has a more limited meaning. **Drawing a conclusion** means making a statement summing up what you have learned from an experiment.

The conclusion of an experiment is usually related to the hypothesis. You may recall that a hypothesis is a possible explanation for a set of observations or answer to a scientific question. After you have carried out the procedure, made and recorded observations, and interpreted the data, you can finally determine whether your experiment showed your hypothesis to be true or false.

Suppose that Leon and Jobelle each write a hypothesis about the summer temperatures where they live.

Example 1: Leon writes, *Summer days are warmest about noon.*

Example 2: Jobelle writes, *The hottest time of the day is about 3 o'clock in the afternoon.*

They test their hypotheses by measuring the outdoor temperature several times a day for the month of July. Then they average their data and graph the data as shown at the right.

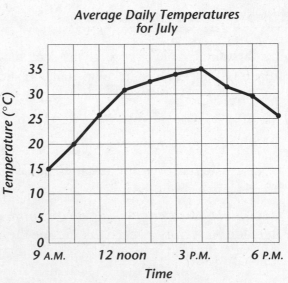

Average Daily Temperatures for July

Skills and Content Review

From the graph, Leon can see that the results of the investigation do not support his hypothesis. He draws this conclusion: *Based on a study of temperatures between 9 A.M. and 6 P.M., the warmest temperatures do not occur about noon but happen sometime later in the afternoon.*

The results do support Jobelle's hypothesis, however. She draws the following conclusion: *On sunny days in July, the warmest temperatures occur about 3 P.M.*

Before scientists become confident of their conclusions, they often repeat their experiments many times and compare their work with that of others. Additional experiments may provide further support for a particular hypothesis. Alternatively, they may cause a researcher to revise or replace the hypothesis.

Tips for Drawing Conclusions

◆ Refer to the hypothesis for your experiment.

◆ Review the observations in your experiment. Analyze the data, completing whatever calculations or graphs you need to help you identify trends or patterns in your results.

◆ Determine whether your data support your hypothesis or suggest that it is false. Write a statement summing up what your results show.

◆ Consider whether you might plan other experiments to support your conclusion or compare your work with that done by other researchers.

Creating Data Tables

Suppose that your class decides to sponsor a Scrabble® competition to raise money. You'll ask people to pay $1.00 each to play. The money will go to a charity that your class has chosen. To keep track of the results, all players will have official score cards that show the number of games they play, their wins and losses, their game scores, and their average score. The easiest way to show all that information would be in a data table.

A **data table** is an organized arrangement of information in labeled rows and columns. Data tables are helpful in many kinds of situations. In science, they are particularly useful when you record observations during an investigation. Making data tables may also help you interpret information that someone else has collected.

Planning a data table is an important part of designing an experiment. A data table provides an orderly way for you to record observations. It can help you keep complete records by reminding you of everything you need to observe. Also, data tables can provide spaces for the results of calculations you plan to do as you interpret the data.

When you create a data table, start by identifying the manipulated and responding variables. For example, suppose you are comparing two types of fertilizer to see whether one of them makes plants grow taller. Your manipulated variable is the type of fertilizer. Your responding variable is the height of the plants. You decide you will measure the height of the plants once a day for a period of three weeks. You also decide to include a control—a plant that receives no fertilizer. You might make a table like the one below.

Effects of Fertilizer on Plant Growth			
Time (days)	**Height of Plant (cm)**		
	Control Plant (no fertilizer)	**Fertilizer A**	**Fertilizer B**
Day 1			
Day 2			
Day 3			

Check your plan to be sure that your data table has a column for each kind of information you will observe and a row for each occasion when you'll make an observation. Be sure to label the columns and rows accurately and identify the units of measurement you are using. And be sure to give the data table a title.

Review the draft of your table to be sure it has places for all the data you plan to collect. For example, in an experiment on the effects of plant fertilizer, you might want to insert columns to record the daily temperature or additional changes in the plants, such as the number of leaves that develop. When your review is complete, create the final data table in your notebook.

▶ Tips for Creating Data Tables

◆ Consider the manipulated and responding variables to determine what observations you will be making.

◆ If you plan to make observations according to a regular pattern, such as once a day, once an hour, or once every five minutes, plan to show those times in the data table.

◆ Make a draft of your table. Show all the columns and rows you'll need and what labels they will have. Be sure to write a title for your table.

◆ Insert units into the column labels where they are needed.

◆ Compare the draft of the data table to the plan for your experiment to be sure you have a place to record all observations you expect to make.

◆ Revise the draft of your data table and draw the final table in your notebook.

Creating Bar Graphs

Each day, some students are absent from school because of illness or other factors. Suppose you are given a list of the number of students absent in grades 6 through 9 today. You are asked to graph the data so that the principal can easily compare the absences across the grades. Which type of graph should you use: bar, circle, or line?

Today's Absences	
Grade	**Number**
6	7
7	9
8	12
9	4

The type of graph you should make depends on your data. Here, the absences in each grade are distinct, or separate, categories. For example, the number of 9th grade absences is distinct from the number of 8th grade absences. You should make a bar graph.

Today's Absences

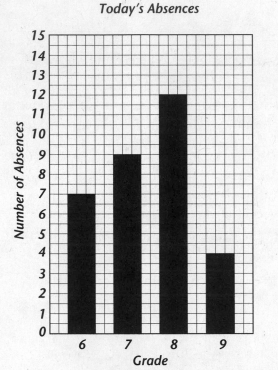

A bar graph is a diagram in which data about separate but related items are represented by rectangular shapes called bars. You usually place the categories being studied on the horizontal axis. Place the measurements or amounts on the vertical axis. The measurement for each category is represented by a separate bar. The length of the bar indicates the amount of the measurement.

Skills and Content Review

In science, bar graphs usually have simple rectangular shapes to indicate the measurements. Sometimes in newspaper and magazines, bar graphs use drawings that represent the measurements. For example, each absent student could be represented by the drawing of a person. For larger numbers, a drawing could stand for 10 students. But regardless of the way the measurement is represented, bar graphs make it easy to read and compare the separate but related data.

▶ **Tips for Creating Bar Graphs**

1. Organize your data in a table. A table makes it easier for you to construct a graph.

2. Draw horizontal and vertical axes on a sheet of graph paper.

3. Place the category being studied, or the manipulated variable, on the horizontal axis. Place the measurements that have been made, or the responding variable, on the vertical axis. Label both axes.

4. Determine the scale for the measurements to be shown on the vertical axis. Choose a scale that lets you represent all the values in your data table. Each square on the graph paper will represent a certain amount. All squares have the same value. In the example on the previous page, each square on the vertical axis represents one absent student.

5. On the horizontal axis, show a bar for each category being represented. Use an equal number of squares for the width of each bar and leave a space of at least one square between the bars. In this example, three squares are used for each bar. A space of two squares has been left between the bars.

6. Using your data, draw in the bars. Remember, all the bars must have the same width.

7. Write a title for your bar graph.

Creating Line Graphs

A science class studying frogs counted the number of times the frogs croaked at different temperatures. The results are shown in the data table on the right. To help interpret that data, the class then created a line graph. A **line graph** is used to display data that show how one variable (the responding variable) changes in response to another variable (the manipulated variable). You should use a line graph when your manipulated variable is continuous, that is, when there are other measurements possible between the ones you tested. For example, in this experiment, temperature is a continuous variable, since 27°C is between 26° and 28°, and 22.5°C is between 22° and 23°. Temperature, time, mass, and velocity are just a few examples of continuous variables.

Number of Croaks vs. Temperature	
Air Temperature in °C	**Frog Croaks per Minute**
22	12
23	14
24	15
26	16
28	17
31	21
32	26

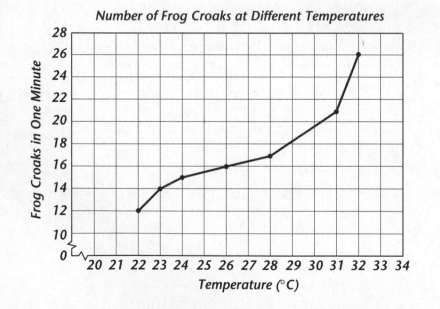

Number of Frog Croaks at Different Temperatures

A line graph is a powerful tool because it shows a relationship between two variables. Here, the line graph shows how the number of frog croaks per minute changes as temperature changes. Line graphs also allow you to identify trends and relationships in the data, and thus infer values you did not actually measure. For example, you can infer that at 30°C, the frogs might make 20 croaks per minute. At 20°C, they might make about 10 croaks per minute. (To find out whether these inferences were true, you would have to do additional research.)

Creating Line Graphs (continued)

What Is a Best Fit Line Graph? Notice that, unlike the graph on the previous page, the lines on the graphs below were not drawn from point to point. Instead, the graphs are smooth and continuous. They flow through as many of the data points as possible but do not necessarily touch all the points. This kind of graph is called a "best fit graph." A best fit graph shows an average, a trend, or a pattern in the data.

You may wonder how scientists know when to use a best fit graph. As you continue to study science, you will see that certain kinds of graphs commonly result from scientific experiments. The graphs shown below are three examples.

The first graph shows a straight line, or linear relationship. (Notice that the word *linear* comes from the word *line*.) You can read that straight-line graph to see that as the volume of a liquid (the manipulated variable) increases, the mass of that liquid (the responding variable) also increases.

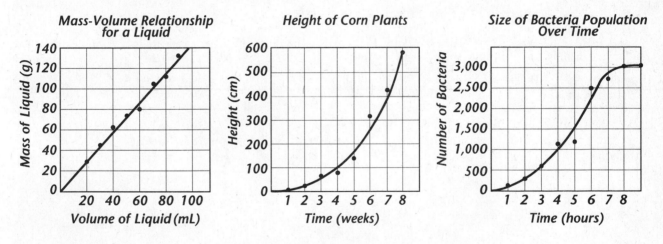

The graphs in the center and on the right are described as nonlinear, meaning they are not straight lines. The center graph shows a curve that continues to rise. You can read that graph to see that over time (the manipulated variable), a corn plant's height (the responding variable) continues to increase.

The graph on the right shows a curve that rises and then flattens out. Here, as time (the manipulated variable) passes, the size of the bacteria population (the responding variable) increases steadily until it reaches a certain size. Then, the size of the population becomes constant.

Look for these and other patterns as you examine additional graphs. Recognizing the pattern of a graph will help you to understand the actual events it represents.

© Pearson Education, Inc.

SCIENCE SKILLS

Skills and Content Review

33

Creating Line Graphs (continued)

▶ Tips for Creating Line Graphs

1. On graph paper, draw a horizontal, or *x*-, axis and a vertical, or *y*-, axis.

2. Label the horizontal axis with the name of the manipulated variable. Label the vertical axis with the name of the responding variable. Include the units of measure.

3. Create a scale on each axis by marking off equally spaced numbers along the axis. Begin with zero or a number slightly less than the smallest number to be graphed. Be sure that each scale covers the entire range of data collected for that variable. Label the units on each scale.

4. Plot each point where the variables intersect. You can do this by following an imaginary line up from the measurement on the *x*-axis. Then follow a second imaginary line across from the corresponding measurement on the *y*-axis. Place a dot where the two lines intersect.

5. Consider whether you will plot from point to point or make a best fit graph. If you plot from point to point, each segment connecting two adjacent points should be straight. If you make a best fit graph, the connecting line should be smooth.

6. Give your graph a title that identifies the variables or the relationship between the variables in the graph. On page 32, "Number of Frog Croaks at Different Temperatures" is a complete title that clearly describes the graph.

Creating Circle Graphs

Suppose that you order an eight-slice pizza for yourself and two friends. The illustration below shows how many pieces each person eats.

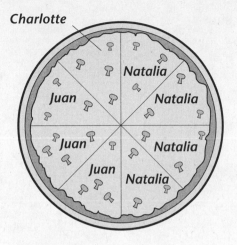

Charlotte

You can change this illustration into a circle graph. A **circle graph** shows data as parts of a whole. The circle represents the whole, or total. The wedges, or segments, represent the parts. Because it resembles a pie cut into slices, a circle graph is sometimes called a pie graph or pie chart.

If you change the pizza illustration into a circle graph, the whole circle will represent the complete pizza. The segments of the graph will show the part of the pizza that each person ate. Look at the data table to see how the number of pieces can be changed into percentages. In a circle graph, all of the parts add up to the total, or 100%.

Amount of Pizza Eaten		
Person	**Number of Pieces**	**Percent of Pizza**
Natalia	4	50%
Juan	3	37.5%
Charlotte	1	12.5%

Like bar graphs, circle graphs can be used to display data in a number of separate categories. Unlike bar graphs, however, circle graphs can be used only when you have data for all the categories that make up the whole.

© Pearson Education, Inc.

Creating Circle Graphs (continued)

▶ ## Tips for Creating Circle Graphs

Kinds of Ads on Children's TV Shows

Type of Product	Number of Ads
Toys	70
Breakfast foods	50
Fast food and drinks	50
Other products	30

1. Organize your data into a table or list. For example, the data table on the right shows information about 200 ads shown on children's TV shows.

2. To find the size of the wedge for each type of product, set up a proportion. Let x equal the number of degrees in that wedge. Then cross-multiply and solve for x. Since there are 360 degrees in a circle, each proportion will read as shown on the right:

$$\frac{\text{Number of ads for product type}}{\text{Total number of ads}} = \frac{x}{360°}$$

For Toys: $\quad \dfrac{70}{200} = \dfrac{x}{360°}$

$$70 \times 360° = x \times 200$$

$$\frac{70 \times 360°}{200} = x$$

$$126° = x$$

Number of Ads	70	50	50	30
Size of Wedge	126°	90°	90°	54°

3. Use a compass to draw a circle. Mark the center of the circle. Then use a straightedge to draw a line from the center point to the top of the circle.

4. Use a protractor to measure the angle of the first wedge, using the line you just drew as the 0° line. For example, the wedge for Toys is 126°. Draw a line from the center of the circle to the edge for the angle you measured.

5. Write a label on the wedge to show what it represents. If there is not enough space in the wedge, write the label outside the circle and draw a line to the wedge.

6. Continue around the circle, drawing in and labeling the other wedges. For each new wedge, use the edge of the last wedge as your 0° line.

7. Determine the percentage that each wedge represents by dividing the number of degrees in the wedge by 360°.

For Toys: $\quad \dfrac{126°}{360°} \times 100\% = 35\%$

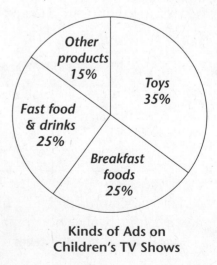

Kinds of Ads on Children's TV Shows

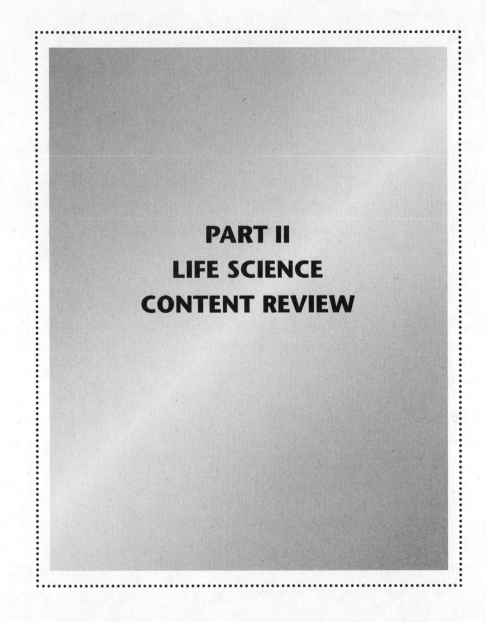

PART II
LIFE SCIENCE
CONTENT REVIEW

TOPIC 1

FROM BACTERIA TO PLANTS

Chapter 1: Living Things

Chapter 2: Viruses and Bacteria

Chapter 3: Protists and Fungi

Chapter 4: Introduction to Plants

Chapter 5: Seed Plants

SECTION 1 — What Is Life?

Key Ideas

◆ Living things have a cellular organization, contain similar chemicals, use energy, grow and develop, respond to their surroundings, and reproduce.

◆ All living things must satisfy their basic needs for energy, water, living space, and stable internal conditions.

Key Terms

organism	response	manipulated
cell	reproduce	variable
unicellular	spontaneous	autotroph
multicellular	generation	heterotroph
development	controlled	homeostasis
stimulus	experiment	

NEEDS OF ORGANISMS

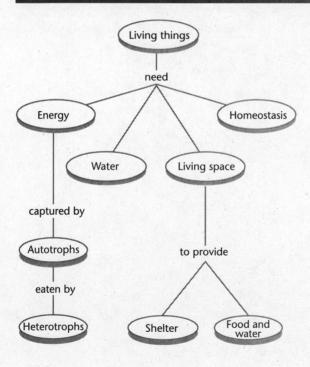

SECTION 2 — The Origin of Life

Key Ideas

◆ Earth's atmosphere 3.6 billion years ago differed greatly from today's atmosphere.

◆ Scientists hypothesize that the small chemical units of life formed in Earth's ancient oceans.

Key Term

fossil

SECTION 3 — Classifying Organisms

Key Ideas

◆ Biologists use classification to organize living things into groups.

◆ Today, organisms are classified into seven levels from kingdom to species.

Key Terms

classification	genus
taxonomy	species
binomial	evolution
nomenclature	taxonomic key

SECTION 4 — The Six Kingdoms

Key Ideas

◆ All organisms are grouped into six kingdoms: archaebacteria, eubacteria, protists, fungi, plants, and animals.

◆ Some characteristics used to classify organisms into kingdoms are cell structure, the way organisms obtain food, and the number of cells in organisms.

Key Terms

prokaryote	nucleus	eukaryote

LIFE SCIENCE

SECTION 1 Viruses

Key Ideas

◆ Viruses are considered to be nonliving because viruses are not cells, and they do not use energy to grow and develop, or to respond to their surroundings.

◆ All viruses have two basic parts: an outer coat that protects the virus and an inner core made of genetic material.

◆ Once inside a cell, a virus uses the host cell's functions to make its own proteins and genetic material. The proteins and genetic material assemble into new viruses, which burst out, destroying the host.

Key Terms

virus

host

parasite

bacteriophage

SECTION 2 Bacteria

Key Ideas

◆ Bacteria are prokaryotes. Their cells do not have nuclei that contain the cell's genetic material. Instead, the genetic material floats freely in the cytoplasm.

◆ Bacteria reproduce asexually by binary fission, which results in the production of two cells exactly like the parent cell. Some bacteria have a simple form of sexual reproduction called conjugation. This process results in a cell with a new combination of genetic information.

◆ Bacteria play positive roles in the lives of humans. Bacteria are involved in fuel and food production, in environmental recycling and cleanup, and in the production of medicines.

Key Terms

cytoplasm

ribosome

flagellum

binary fission

asexual reproduction

sexual reproduction

conjugation

respiration

endospore

decomposer

SECTION 3 Viruses, Bacteria, and Your Health

Key Ideas

◆ Infectious disease can spread through contact with an infected person, a contaminated object, an infected animal, or an environmental source.

◆ There is no cure for viral diseases. Bacterial diseases can be cured through the use of antibiotics. Vaccines can prevent some viral and bacterial diseases.

Key Terms

infectious disease

toxin

antibiotic

vaccine

COMPARING VIRUSES AND BACTERIA

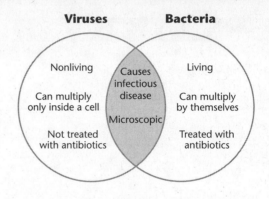

Viruses

Bacteria

Nonliving

Can multiply only inside a cell

Not treated with antibiotics

Causes infectious disease

Microscopic

Living

Can multiply by themselves

Treated with antibiotics

Skills and Content Review

SECTION 1   Protists

Key Ideas

◆ Animal-like protists, or protozoans, include sarcodines, ciliates, zooflagellates, and sporozoans. Like animals, these protists are heterotrophs. Most protozoans move by using pseudopods, cilia, or flagella.

◆ Funguslike protists include water molds, downy mildews, and slime molds. Like fungi, these protists are heterotrophs, have cell walls, and use spores to reproduce.

◆ Plantlike protists, or algae, include euglenoids, dinoflagellates, diatoms, green algae, red algae, and brown algae. Like plants, these organisms are autotrophs.

Key Terms

protozoan	mutualism
pseudopod	spore
contractile vacuole	algae
cilia	pigment
symbiosis	

SECTION 2   Algal Blooms

Key Ideas

◆ Red tides occur when a population of algae increases quickly in ocean waters. Some algae can secrete toxins that poison animals.

◆ Nutrients in a lake or pond build up over time, causing an increase in the numbers of algae. An accelerated rate of eutrophication can lead to the deaths of many organisms in the lake or pond.

Key Terms

algal bloom	eutrophication
red tide	

THE EFFECT OF EXCESS NUTRIENTS IN A LAKE

Excess nutrients flow into a lake.

↓

Algal bloom occurs.

↓

Excess algae block the sun and plants on the bottom die.

↓

As decomposers feed on the dead bodies, they use up the oxygen in the water.

↓

The fishes and other organisms in the water die.

SECTION 3   Fungi

Key Ideas

◆ Most fungi are eukaryotes, use spores to reproduce, and are heterotrophs.

◆ Most fungi feed by absorbing food through their hyphae. The hyphae secrete digestive chemicals into a food source, which is broken down into small substances that are absorbed by the hyphae.

◆ Fungi produce spores in fruiting bodies. Most fungi reproduce both asexually and sexually.

◆ Fungi are decomposers that recycle Earth's chemicals.

Key Terms

hypha	budding
fruiting body	lichen

LIFE SCIENCE

LIFE SCIENCE

SECTION 1 The Plant Kingdom

Key Ideas

◆ Plants are autotrophs. All plants are also multicellular eukaryotes.

◆ Plant cells have cell walls that are made mostly of cellulose. Plant cells contain chloroplasts, in which food is made, and vacuoles that store water, food, and other substances.

◆ All plants have complex life cycles. In the sporophyte stage, plants produce spores. In the gametophyte stage, plants produce sperm cells and egg cells.

◆ For plants to survive on land, they need ways to obtain water and other materials from their surroundings, retain moisture, support their bodies, transport materials throughout the plant, and reproduce successfully.

Key Terms

photosynthesis	tissue	zygote
cell wall	chlorophyll	sporophyte
cellulose	cuticle	gametophyte
chloroplast	vascular tissue	gamete
vacuole	fertilization	

SECTION 2 Photosynthesis and Light

Key Ideas

◆ White light is made up of the different colors of the rainbow—red, orange, yellow, green, blue, and violet.

◆ Most of the light that strikes a leaf is absorbed by pigments in the chloroplasts of the cells. Chlorophyll, the main pigment, absorbs red and blue light. Light energy powers the process of photosynthesis.

◆ In photosynthesis, carbon dioxide and water are converted into sugars and oxygen using the light energy.

Key Term

accessory pigment

SECTION 3 Mosses, Liverworts, and Hornworts

Key Ideas

◆ Nonvascular plants are small, low-growing plants that lack vascular tissue. Most nonvascular plants transport materials by passing them from one cell to the next.

◆ Mosses, liverworts, and hornworts are three types of nonvascular plants.

Key Terms

nonvascular plant	bog
rhizoid	peat

SECTION 4 Ferns and Their Relatives

Key Ideas

◆ Seedless vascular plants have vascular tissue and use spores to reproduce. These plants include ferns, club mosses, and horsetails.

◆ Seedless vascular plants grow taller than nonvascular plants. The plants' spores are released into the environment, where they grow into gametophytes.

Key Terms

vascular plant	frond

CHARACTERISTICS OF MOSSES AND FERNS

Characteristic	Mosses	Ferns
Size	Small and low	Can be tall
Environment	Moist	Moist
Body parts	Rootlike, stemlike, and leaflike	Fronds, stems, and roots
Familiar generation	Gametophyte	Sporophyte
Vascular tissue present?	No	Yes

Seed Plants

 SECTION 1 The Characteristics of Seed Plants

Key Ideas

◆ All seed plants have vascular tissue and produce seeds. All seed plants also have leaves, stems, and roots.

◆ A seed has three important parts: an embryo, stored food, and a seed coat.

◆ Photosynthesis occurs mainly in leaves. Stems support plants and transport materials. Roots anchor plants and absorb water and minerals.

Key Terms

phloem	cotyledon	transpiration
xylem	germination	cambium
seed	stomata	root cap
embryo		

SECTION 2 Gymnosperms

Key Ideas

◆ All gymnosperms produce naked seeds. Many gymnosperms also have needlelike or scalelike leaves, and grow deep root systems.

◆ During reproduction, pollen falls onto a female cone. A sperm cell and an egg cell join. The zygote develops into the seed's embryo.

Key Terms

gymnosperm	pollen	pollination
cone	ovule	

 SECTION 3 Angiosperms

Key Ideas

◆ Angiosperms produce flowers and fruits.

◆ During reproduction, pollen falls on the stigma. In time, the sperm cell and egg cell join in the ovule. The zygote develops into the seed's embryo.

Key Terms

angiosperm	sepal	fruit
ovary	stamen	monocot
flower	pistil	dicot
petal		

 SECTION 4 Plant Responses and Growth

Key Ideas

◆ A tropism is a plant's growth response toward or away from a stimulus. Plants respond to touch, light, and gravity.

◆ Plant hormones control tropisms and many other plant functions.

Key Terms

tropism	hormone	auxin

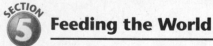 **SECTION 5 Feeding the World**

Key Ideas

◆ Genetic engineering, precision farming, and hydroponics can help farmers produce more crops to feed the world's population.

Key Terms

genetic engineering   hydroponics

LIFE SCIENCE

TOPIC 2

ANIMALS

1 What Is an Animal?

Key Ideas

◆ Animals are multicellular organisms that obtain food by eating other organisms.

◆ Animals need water, food, and oxygen to survive. Some animals are carnivores, or meat eaters. Others are herbivores, or plant eaters. Omnivores eat both plants and animals.

◆ Some animals are vertebrates; most animal species are invertebrates.

Key Terms

species	asexual	prey
organ	reproduction	omnivore
heterotroph	adaptation	phylum
autotroph	herbivore	invertebrate
sexual	carnivore	vertebrate
reproduction	predator	

2 Symmetry

Key Ideas

◆ The bodies of complex animals all have either radial or bilateral symmetry.

◆ Animals with radial symmetry have body parts arranged around a central point.

◆ Animals with bilateral symmetry have one line that divides them into two mirror images.

Key Terms

bilateral symmetry   radial symmetry

3 Sponges and Cnidarians

Key Ideas

◆ A sponge obtains food by straining water taken in through its pores.

◆ Cnidarians are carnivores with stinging cells that help capture prey.

◆ Corals are cnidarians with hard skeletons around their soft bodies.

Key Terms

larva	polyp
cnidarian	medusa

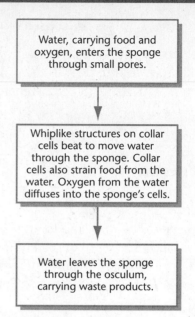

WATER MOVEMENT THROUGH A SPONGE

Water, carrying food and oxygen, enters the sponge through small pores.

↓

Whiplike structures on collar cells beat to move water through the sponge. Collar cells also strain food from the water. Oxygen from the water diffuses into the sponge's cells.

↓

Water leaves the sponge through the osculum, carrying waste products.

4 Worms

Key Ideas

◆ The three major worm phyla are flatworms, roundworms, and segmented worms.

◆ Most flatworms are parasites that obtain food from their hosts. Planarians are nonparasitic flatworms.

◆ Roundworms have a digestive system that is a tube open at both ends.

◆ Segmented worms have bodies made up of many segments. Segmented worms have a closed circulatory system in which blood is contained in blood vessels.

Key Terms

regeneration	host
parasite	anus

© Pearson Education, Inc.

LIFE SCIENCE

Chapter 2   Mollusks, Arthropods, and Echinoderms

SECTION 1   Mollusks

Key Ideas
◆ Most mollusks have shells, soft bodies, a mantle covering internal organs, and a muscular foot.
◆ Major groups of mollusks include gastropods, bivalves, and cephalopods.

Key Terms
mollusk	radula	bivalve
kidney	gastropod	cephalopod
gill		

SECTION 2   Arthropods

Key Ideas
◆ Arthropods have an exoskeleton, jointed appendages, and a segmented body.
◆ Major groups of arthropods include crustaceans, arachnids, centipedes, millipedes, and insects.

Key Terms
arthropod	molting	metamorphosis
exoskeleton	antenna	arachnid
chitin	crustacean	abdomen

CLASSIFICATION OF ARTHROPODS

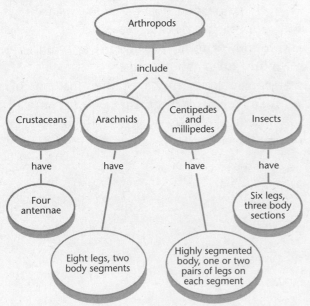

SECTION 3   Insects

Key Ideas
◆ Insects are arthropods with three body sections, six legs, one pair of antennae, and usually one or two pairs of wings.
◆ An insect undergoing complete metamorphosis goes through four distinct stages—egg, larva, pupa, and adult. An insect undergoing gradual metamorphosis hatches from an egg to a nymph; the nymph may molt several times before becoming an adult.

Key Terms
insect	pupa
thorax	gradual metamorphosis
complete metamorphosis	nymph
	camouflage

SECTION 4   The Sounds of Insects

Key Ideas
◆ Sound is generated by something that vibrates. Sound travels in waves through solids, liquids, and gases.
◆ Many insects use sound to attract mates.

SECTION 5   Echinoderms

Key Ideas
◆ Echinoderms have an endoskeleton, five-part radial symmetry, and a water vascular system.
◆ Echinoderms include sea stars, sea urchins, brittle stars, and sea cucumbers.

Key Terms
echinoderm	water vascular system
endoskeleton	

Skills and Content Review

What Is a Vertebrate?

Key Ideas

◆ Vertebrates have a backbone that is part of an endoskeleton. The endoskeleton supports, protects, and gives shape to the body.

◆ Most fishes, amphibians, and reptiles are ectotherms. Mammals and birds are endotherms.

Key Terms

chordate	notochord	cartilage
vertebra	ectotherm	endotherm

 **Fishes**

Key Ideas

◆ A fish is a vertebrate that lives in the water and has fins. Most fishes are ectotherms, obtain oxygen through gills, and have scales.

◆ Major groups of fishes include jawless fishes, cartilaginous fishes, and bony fishes.

Key Terms

fish	swim bladder	buoyant force

THE CHARACTERISTICS OF DIFFERENT FISH GROUPS

Kind of Fish	Kind of Skeleton	Jaws?	Scales?	Example
Jawless Fishes	cartilage	no	none	lamprey
Cartilagenous Fishes	cartilage	yes	toothlike scales	shark
Bony Fishes	bone	yes	yes	trout

Amphibians

Key Ideas

◆ An amphibian is a moist-skinned, ectothermic vertebrate. Most amphibians spend their early lives in water and adulthood on land, returning to water to reproduce.

◆ Major groups of amphibians include frogs, toads, and salamanders.

◆ Adult amphibians have strong skeletons and muscular limbs adapted for moving on land.

Key Terms

amphibian	atrium	ventricle
habitat		

Reptiles

Key Ideas

◆ A reptile is an ectothermic vertebrate that has lungs and scaly skin. Reptiles can spend their entire lives on dry land.

◆ The leathery eggs, scaly skin, and the kidneys of reptiles are adapted to conserving water.

◆ Major groups of reptiles include lizards, snakes, turtles, and alligators and crocodiles.

Key Terms

reptile	urine

Vertebrate History in Rocks

Key Ideas

◆ Sedimentary rock forms from hardened layers of sediments such as clay, mud, or sand.

◆ Fossils are found primarily in sedimentary rock.

◆ Paleontologists study fossils to infer how organisms, including vertebrates, have changed over time.

Key Terms

fossil	sedimentary rock	paleontologist

LIFE SCIENCE

LIFE SCIENCE

SECTION 1 Birds

Key Ideas

◆ Birds are endothermic vertebrates that have feathers and a four-chambered heart and lay eggs. Most birds can fly.

◆ Birds care for their young by keeping the eggs warm until hatching and by protecting the young at least until they can fly.

◆ Birds have adaptations, such as the shapes of their toes and bills, for living and obtaining food in different environments.

Key Terms

bird	down feather	crop
contour feather	insulator	gizzard

SECTION 2 The Physics of Bird Flight

Key Ideas

◆ Air flowing over the curved upper surface of a moving wing exerts less downward pressure than the upward pressure from the air flowing beneath the wing. The difference in pressure produces lift that causes the wing to rise.

◆ Birds fly by flapping, soaring, and gliding.

Key Term

lift

SECTION 3 What Is a Mammal?

Key Ideas

◆ Mammals are vertebrates that are endothermic, have skin covered with hair or fur, feed their young with milk from the mother's mammary glands, and have teeth of different shapes adapted to their diets.

◆ Mammals use a large muscle called the diaphragm to breathe. Mammals have a four-chambered heart and a two-loop circulation.

Key Terms

mammal	premolars	diaphragm
incisors	molars	mammary gland
canines		

SECTION 4 Diversity of Mammals

Key Ideas

◆ Mammals are classified into three groups on the basis of how their young develop. Monotremes lay eggs. Marsupials give birth to live young who continue to develop in the mother's pouch. The young of placental mammals develop more fully before birth than do the young of marsupials.

◆ Placental mammals are divided into groups on the basis of adaptations, such as those for feeding and moving.

Key Terms

monotreme	placental mammal
marsupial	placenta
gestation period	

© Pearson Education, Inc.

THE CHARACTERISTICS OF MAMMAL GROUPS

Characteristic	Monotremes	Marsupials	Placental Mammals
How Young Begin Life	in eggs	in their mother's pouch	at an advanced stage of development
How Young Are Fed	milk from pores or slits on mother's skin	milk from nipples in their mother's pouch	milk from nipples
Example	spiny anteater	kangaroo	human

SECTION 1 — Why Do Animals Behave as They Do?

Key Ideas

◆ Most behaviors help an animal survive and reproduce.

◆ An instinct is an inborn behavior pattern that the animal performs correctly the first time.

◆ Learning changes an animal's behavior as a result of experience.

◆ Imprinting, in which very young animals learn to follow the first moving object they see, involves both instinct and learning.

Key Terms

behavior	conditioning
stimulus	trial-and-error learning
response	insight learning
instinct	artificial intelligence
learning	imprinting

THREE TYPES OF LEARNING

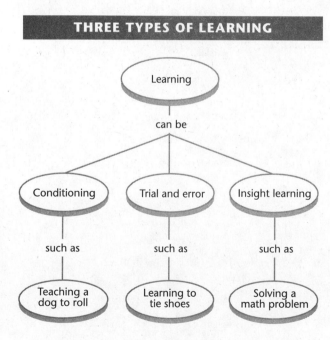

SECTION 2 — Patterns of Behavior

Key Ideas

◆ Animals use aggression to compete for limited resources, such as food or shelter.

◆ Many animals establish territories from which they exclude other members of their species.

◆ Courtship behavior ensures that males and females of the same species recognize one another so that they can reproduce.

◆ There is usually some survival advantage to living in a group.

◆ Animals use chemicals, sounds, body positions, and movements to communicate.

◆ Some animal behaviors, such as circadian rhythms, occur in regular patterns.

◆ Some animals migrate to places where they can more easily find food, reproduce, or both.

Key Terms

aggression	circadian rhythm
territory	hibernation
courtship behavior	migration
society	

SECTION 3 — The Chemistry of Communication

Key Ideas

◆ Pheromones are chemicals that animals use to establish a territory, locate food, attract a mate, and identify group members.

◆ Bioluminescence is the production of light by a living organism.

Key Terms

pheromone	bioluminescence

TOPIC 3

CELLS AND HEREDITY

LIFE SCIENCE

SECTION 1   Discovering Cells

Key Ideas
◆ The invention of the microscope made the discovery of the cell possible.
◆ The cell theory states that: all living things are made of cells; cells are the basic units of life; all cells come from other cells.

Key Terms
cell
microscope
compound microscope
cell theory

magnification
convex lens
resolution

SECTION 2   Looking Inside Cells

Key Ideas
◆ The cell membrane protects the cell and controls what substances enter and leave it.
◆ The nucleus is the cell's control center.
◆ Organelles in the cytoplasm perform many vital functions.

Key Terms
organelle	cytoplasm	Golgi body
cell wall	mitochondrion	chloroplast
cell membrane	endoplasmic	vacuole
nucleus	reticulum	lysosome
chromatin	ribosome	

SECTION 3   Chemical Compounds in Cells

Key Ideas
◆ The main groups of organic compounds found in living things are carbohydrates, lipids, proteins, and nucleic acids.
◆ Without water, most chemical reactions within cells could not take place.

Key Terms
element	inorganic	enzyme
atom	compound	lipid
compound	carbohydrate	nucleic acid
molecule	protein	DNA
organic compound	amino acid	RNA

TYPES OF ORGANIC COMPOUNDS

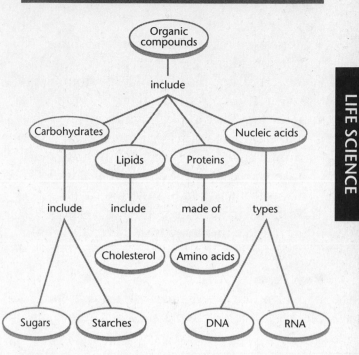

SECTION 4   The Cell in Its Environment

Key Ideas
◆ Substances can move into and out of a cell by diffusion, osmosis, or active transport.
◆ Diffusion is the process by which molecules move from an area of higher concentration to an area of lower concentration. Osmosis is the diffusion of water molecules through a selectively permeable membrane.
◆ Active transport requires the cell to use energy while passive transport does not.
◆ If a cell grew too large, it could not function well enough to survive.

Key Terms
selectively permeable
diffusion
osmosis

passive transport
active transport

LIFE SCIENCE

1 Photosynthesis

Key Ideas

◆ During photosynthesis, plants and some other organisms use energy from the sun to convert carbon dioxide and water into oxygen and sugars, including glucose.

◆ In the first stage of photosynthesis, chlorophyll and other plant pigments capture energy from sunlight. In the second stage, the cell uses the energy to produce sugars from carbon dioxide and water.

◆ Nearly all living things obtain the energy they need either directly or indirectly from the sun.

Key Terms

photosynthesis	chlorophyll	autotroph
pigment	stomata	heterotroph

2 Respiration

Key Ideas

◆ Respiration is a process in which cells break down simple food substances, such as glucose, and release the energy they contain.

◆ During respiration, glucose and oxygen are converted into carbon dioxide and water.

◆ Photosynthesis and respiration can be thought of as opposite processes. These two processes form a cycle that keeps the levels of oxygen and carbon dioxide fairly constant in the atmosphere.

◆ Fermentation provides energy for cells without using oxygen.

Key Terms

respiration   fermentation

3 Cell Division

Key Ideas

◆ Cells go through a cycle of growth and division called the cell cycle. The phases of the cell cycle are interphase, mitosis, and cytokinesis.

◆ DNA replication ensures that each cell will have all of the genetic information it needs.

Key Terms

cell cycle	mitosis	chromatid
interphase	chromosome	cytokinesis
replication		

THE CELL CYCLE

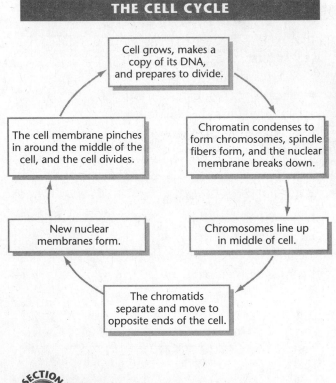

4 Cancer

Key Ideas

◆ Cancer begins when the normal cell cycle is disrupted by mutations, causing cells to divide in an uncontrolled way.

◆ Cancer is usually treated with surgery, radiation, or chemotherapy.

Key Terms

cancer	tumor
mutation	chemotherapy

Mendel's Work

Key Ideas

◆ Gregor Mendel's work was the foundation for understanding why offspring have traits similar to those of their parents.

◆ Traits are controlled by alleles of genes. Organisms inherit one allele from each parent.

◆ Some alleles are dominant and some alleles are recessive.

Key Terms

trait	purebred	dominant allele
heredity	gene	recessive allele
genetics	allele	hybrid

Probability and Genetics

Key Ideas

◆ Probability is the likelihood that a particular event will happen.

◆ Mendel was the first scientist to interpret his data using the principles of probability.

◆ Geneticists use Punnett squares to show all the possible outcomes of a genetic cross.

Key Terms

probability	homozygous
Punnett square	heterozygous
phenotype	codominance
genotype	

The Cell and Inheritance

Key Ideas

◆ According to the chromosome theory of inheritance, genes are carried from parents to their offspring on chromosomes.

◆ During meiosis, chromosome pairs separate to form sex cells. Only one chromosome from each pair ends up in each sex cell. The sex cells have half the number of chromosomes as the body cells.

Key Term

meiosis

The DNA Connection

Key Ideas

◆ The nitrogen bases along a gene form a code that specifies the order in which amino acids will be put together to produce a protein.

◆ During protein synthesis, messenger RNA copies the coded message from the DNA in the nucleus and carries the message into the cytoplasm. Transfer RNA adds amino acids to the growing protein.

◆ A mutation is a change in a gene or chromosome. Some mutations are harmful, some are helpful, and some are neutral.

Key Terms

messenger RNA   transfer RNA

COMPARING DNA AND MESSENGER RNA

Characteristic	DNA	Messenger RNA
Nitrogen bases	Adenine Thymine Guanine Cytosine	Adenine, uracil, guanine, cytosine
Structure	Twisted ladder	One strand of the ladder
Function	Forms a genetic code that specifies what type of protein will be produced	Carries the genetic code from the DNA inside the nucleus into the cytoplasm

LIFE SCIENCE

© Pearson Education, Inc.

Skills and Content Review

LIFE SCIENCE

SECTION 1   Human Inheritance

Key Ideas

◆ Some human traits are controlled by a single gene that has multiple alleles—three or more forms.

◆ Some human traits show a wide range of phenotypes because these traits are controlled by many genes. The genes act together as a group to produce a single trait.

◆ Traits are often influenced by the organism's environment.

◆ Males have one X chromosome and one Y chromosome. Females have two X chromosomes. Males are more likely than females to have a sex-linked trait controlled by a recessive allele.

◆ Geneticists use pedigrees to trace the inheritance pattern of a particular trait through a number of generations of a family.

Key Terms

multiple alleles	carrier
sex-linked gene	pedigree

THE INHERITANCE OF HUMAN TRAITS

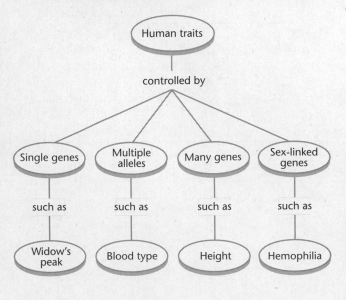

SECTION 2   Human Genetic Disorders

Key Ideas

◆ Genetic disorders are abnormal conditions that are caused by mutations, or DNA changes, in genes or chromosomes.

◆ Common genetic disorders include cystic fibrosis, sickle-cell disease, hemophilia, and Down syndrome.

◆ Amniocentesis and karyotypes are tools used to diagnose genetic disorders.

◆ Genetic counselors help couples understand their chances of having a child with a genetic disorder.

Key Terms

genetic disorder	karyotype
amniocentesis	

SECTION 3   Advances in Genetics

Key Ideas

◆ Selective breeding is the process of selecting a few organisms with desired traits to serve as parents of the next generation.

◆ Cloning is a technique used to produce genetically identical organisms.

◆ Genetic engineering can be used to produce medicines and to improve food crops. Researchers are also using genetic engineering to try to cure human genetic disorders.

◆ DNA fingerprinting can be used to help determine whether material found at a crime scene came from a particular suspect.

◆ The goal of the Human Genome Project is to identify the DNA sequence of every gene in the human genome.

Key Terms

selective breeding	genetic engineering
inbreeding	gene therapy
hybridization	genome
clone	

SECTION 1 — Darwin's Voyage

Key Ideas

◆ Darwin thought that species gradually changed over many generations as they became better adapted to new conditions. This process is called evolution.

◆ Darwin's observations led him to propose that evolution occurs through natural selection. Natural selection occurs due to overproduction, competition, and variations.

◆ Only traits controlled by genes can change over time as a result of natural selection.

◆ If a group of individuals remains separated from the rest of its species long enough to evolve different traits, a new species can form.

Key Terms

species   evolution   natural selection
adaptation   scientific theory   variation

SECTION 2 — The Fossil Record

Key Ideas

◆ Most fossils form when organisms die and sediments bury them. The sediments harden, preserving parts of the organisms.

◆ Relative dating determines which of two fossils is older and which is younger. Absolute dating determines the actual age of a fossil.

◆ Fossils help scientists understand how extinct organisms looked and evolved.

◆ The Geologic Time Scale shows when during Earth's 4.6-billion-year history major groups of organisms evolved.

◆ Evolution has occurred gradually at some times and fairly rapidly at other times.

Key Terms

fossil   radioactive element
sedimentary rock   half-life
petrified fossil   fossil record
mold   extinct
cast   gradualism
relative dating   punctuated equilibria
absolute dating

SECTION 3 — Other Evidence for Evolution

Key Ideas

◆ By comparing modern-day organisms, scientists can infer how closely related they are in an evolutionary sense.

◆ Homologous structures can provide evidence of how species are related and of how they evolved from a common ancestor.

◆ Similarities in early developmental stages are evidence that species are related and shared a common ancestor.

◆ Scientists can compare DNA and protein sequences to determine more precisely how species are related.

◆ A branching tree is a diagram that shows how scientists think different groups of organisms are related.

Key Terms

homologous structure   branching tree

HOW NATURAL SELECTION WORKS

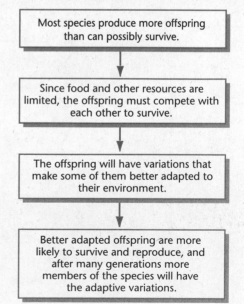

Most species produce more offspring than can possibly survive.

Since food and other resources are limited, the offspring must compete with each other to survive.

The offspring will have variations that make some of them better adapted to their environment.

Better adapted offspring are more likely to survive and reproduce, and after many generations more members of the species will have the adaptive variations.

LIFE SCIENCE

© Pearson Education, Inc.

Skills and Content Review

TOPIC 4

HUMAN BIOLOGY AND HEALTH

SECTION 1   How the Body Is Organized

Key Ideas
◆ The levels of organization in the human body consist of cells, tissues, organs, and organ systems.
◆ The cell is the basic unit of structure and function in living things. The human body contains about 100 trillion cells.
◆ A tissue is a group of cells that perform the same function. The human body contains four basic types of tissue—muscle, nerve, connective, and epithelial.
◆ Organs, which are composed of different kinds of tissue, perform complex functions. An organ system is a group of organs that work together to perform a major function.

Key Terms
cell
cell membrane
nucleus
cytoplasm
tissue
muscle tissue
nerve tissue
connective tissue
epithelial tissue
organ
organ system

SECTION 2   Keeping the Body in Balance

Key Ideas
◆ Homeostasis is the process by which an organism's internal environment is kept stable in spite of changes in the external environment.
◆ Stress disturbs homeostasis. When under stress, the body releases adrenaline, which causes many changes in the body. These changes prepare the body to take quick action.
◆ Exercise and relaxing activities can help relieve stress.

Key Terms
homeostasis   stress   adrenaline

SECTION 3   Wellness

Key Ideas
◆ Wellness means being at the best possible level of health. The three components of wellness are physical health, mental health, and social health.
◆ Physical health involves how well the body functions. Mental health involves how you feel about yourself and how well you handle the demands of your life. Social health is how well you get along with other people.
◆ To make a health-related decision, you should consider both the benefits and the risks of any action.

Key Terms
wellness
physical health
mental health
social health
peer pressure
continuum

THE THREE COMPONENTS OF WELLNESS

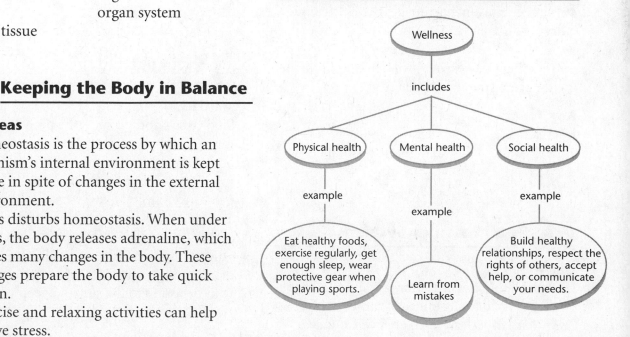

LIFE SCIENCE

SECTION 1 — The Skeletal System

Key Ideas
- The skeleton provides shape and support, enables movement, protects internal organs, produces blood cells, and stores materials.
- Movable joints allow the body to make a wide range of motions. Movable joints include gliding joints, hinge joints, pivot joints, and ball-and-socket joints.
- A combination of a balanced diet and regular exercise helps keep bones healthy.

Key Terms
vertebra	cartilage	ligament
marrow	joint	osteoporosis

SECTION 2 — Diagnosing Bone and Joint Injuries

Key Ideas
- X-rays are used to take images of bones.
- Magnetic resonance imaging (MRI) is used to produce an image of soft tissues.
- Skeletal injuries can be prevented by warming up, wearing protective equipment, and exercising in safe places.

Key Terms
fracture	X-ray
sprain	magnetic resonance
dislocation	imaging

SECTION 3 — The Muscular System

Key Ideas
- Skeletal muscles are voluntary muscles that are attached to the bones of the skeleton. Smooth muscles, which are involuntary muscles, line the walls of many internal organs and blood vessels. Cardiac muscles are involuntary muscles found only in the heart.
- Skeletal muscles work in pairs. When one muscle contracts and shortens, the other muscle in the pair expands and lengthens.

Key Terms
involuntary muscle	smooth muscle
tendon	skeletal muscle
voluntary muscle	cardiac muscle

TYPES OF MUSCLES IN THE HUMAN BODY

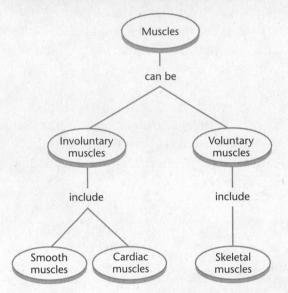

SECTION 4 — The Skin

Key Ideas
- Skin covers and protects the body from injury and infection. It also helps to regulate body temperature, get rid of wastes, gather information about the environment, and produce vitamin D.
- The epidermis is the top layer of the skin. The dermis is the lower layer of the skin.
- For healthy skin, eat a well-balanced diet and drink enough water. Also, you should limit your exposure to the sun and keep your skin clean.

Key Terms
epidermis	pore	cancer
melanin	follicle	acne
dermis		

SECTION 1 — Food and Energy

Key Ideas
◆ The six nutrients necessary for human health are carbohydrates, fats, proteins, vitamins, minerals, and water.
◆ Water is the most important nutrient because it is necessary for all body processes.

Key Terms
nutrient	fat	protein
calorie	unsaturated fat	amino acid
carbohydrate	saturated fat	vitamin
glucose	cholesterol	mineral
fiber		

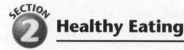

SECTION 2 — Healthy Eating

Key Ideas
◆ The Food Guide Pyramid classifies foods into six major groups and tells how many servings from each group to eat.
◆ Food labels list the nutrients in foods and show how the foods fit into your daily diet.

Key Terms
Food Guide Pyramid   Percent Daily Value

SECTION 3 — The Digestive Process Begins

Key Ideas
◆ The functions of the digestive system are to break down food, absorb food molecules into the blood, and eliminate wastes.
◆ During mechanical digestion, food is ground into small pieces. During chemical digestion, large food molecules are broken into small molecules by enzymes.
◆ Food first passes from the mouth into the esophagus, and then into the stomach. Waves of muscle contractions, known as peristalsis, keep the food moving in one direction.

Key Terms
digestion	enzyme	mucus
absorption	epiglottis	peristalsis
saliva	esophagus	stomach

SECTION 4 — Final Digestion and Absorption

Key Ideas
◆ Almost all chemical digestion and absorption of nutrients takes place in the small intestine.
◆ Nutrients are absorbed into the bloodstream through the villi of the small intestine.
◆ As material moves through the large intestine, water is absorbed. The remaining material is readied for elimination.

Key Terms
small intestine	gallbladder	large intestine
liver	pancreas	rectum
bile	villus	anus

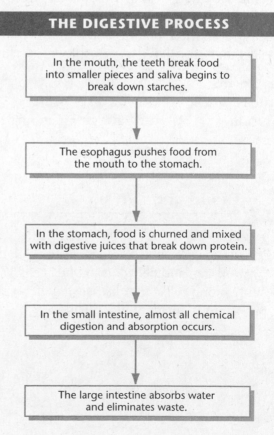

THE DIGESTIVE PROCESS

In the mouth, the teeth break food into smaller pieces and saliva begins to break down starches.

↓

The esophagus pushes food from the mouth to the stomach.

↓

In the stomach, food is churned and mixed with digestive juices that break down protein.

↓

In the small intestine, almost all chemical digestion and absorption occurs.

↓

The large intestine absorbs water and eliminates waste.

LIFE SCIENCE

LIFE SCIENCE

SECTION 1 The Body's Transportation System

Key Ideas
◆ The heart pumps blood through the blood vessels. The heart has four chambers. The two atria receive blood, and the two ventricles pump blood out of the heart.
◆ Blood travels from the heart to the lungs and back to the heart. It is then pumped to the body and returns again to the heart.

Key Terms
cardiovascular system	ventricle	capillary
	valve	vein
heart	pacemaker	aorta
atrium	artery	force

SECTION 2 A Closer Look at Blood Vessels

Key Idea
◆ Arteries carry blood from the heart to the capillaries. In the capillaries, materials are exchanged between the blood and the body's cells. From the capillaries, blood flows into veins that carry it back to the heart.

Key Terms
coronary artery   blood pressure
diffusion   sphygmomanometer
pressure

SECTION 3 Blood and Lymph

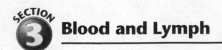

Key Idea
◆ Red blood cells, which contain hemoglobin, carry oxygen and deliver it to body cells. White blood cells fight disease. Platelets are important in forming blood clots.

Key Terms
plasma	fibrin
red blood cell	blood transfusion
hemoglobin	lymphatic system
white blood cell	lymph
platelet	lymph node

SECTION 4 Cardiovascular Health

Key Ideas
◆ Atherosclerosis is a condition in which an artery wall thickens due to the buildup of cholesterol and other fatty materials.
◆ Hypertension is a disorder in which the blood pressure is higher than normal.
◆ To help prevent atherosclerosis and hypertension, people need to exercise regularly; eat a diet low in fat, cholesterol, and salt; and avoid smoking.

Key Terms
atherosclerosis   hypertension
heart attack

THE THREE TYPES OF BLOOD VESSELS

Blood Vessel	Function	Structure of Wall
Artery	carries blood away from the heart	3 layers: inner—epithelial tissue middle—muscle outer—connective tissue
Capillary	exchange of materials between cells and blood	one layer of epithelial cells
Vein	carries blood from the capillaries to the heart	3 layers: inner—epithelial tissue middle—muscle outer—connective tissue

The Respiratory System

Key Ideas

- The respiratory system moves oxygen into the body and removes carbon dioxide from the body.
- In the process of respiration in cells, glucose is broken down using oxygen to produce energy.
- As air travels from the outside environment to the lungs, it passes through the nose, pharynx, trachea, and bronchi.
- In the alveoli, oxygen moves from the air into the blood, while carbon dioxide and water pass from the blood into the air.
- During inhalation, the diaphragm and rib muscles make the chest cavity expand. The air pressure inside the lungs decreases, and air rushes into the lungs. During exhalation, the chest cavity becomes smaller, pushing air out of the body.
- When air passes over the vocal cords, which are folds of tissue in the larynx, they vibrate to produce sound.

Key Terms

respiration	bronchi	diaphragm
cilia	lungs	larynx
pharynx	alveoli	vocal cords
trachea		

 Smoking and Your Health

Key Ideas

- The most harmful substances in tobacco smoke are tar, carbon monoxide, and nicotine.
- When people inhale tobacco smoke, they increase their chances of developing respiratory diseases such as chronic bronchitis, emphysema, and lung cancer.
- Smokers are more likely to have heart attacks than are nonsmokers.

Key Terms

tar	bronchitis
carbon monoxide	emphysema
nicotine	passive smoking
addiction	

 The Excretory System

Key Ideas

- The excretory system removes carbon dioxide, urea, water, and other wastes from the body.
- The kidneys are the major organs of excretion. By filtering the blood, the kidneys produce urine.
- Urine travels from the kidneys through the ureters to the urinary bladder.
- In the kidney's nephrons, wastes and other materials are filtered from the blood. Some useful substances, such as glucose and water, are then reabsorbed into the blood.
- The lungs, skin, and liver are also organs of excretion.

Key Terms

excretion	urine	urethra
urea	ureters	nephron
kidney	urinary bladder	

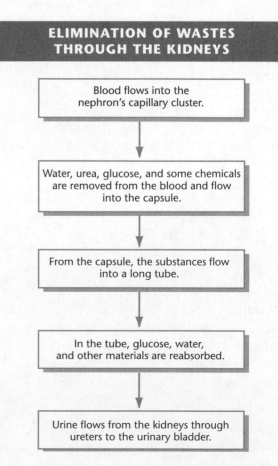

ELIMINATION OF WASTES THROUGH THE KIDNEYS

Blood flows into the nephron's capillary cluster.

↓

Water, urea, glucose, and some chemicals are removed from the blood and flow into the capsule.

↓

From the capsule, the substances flow into a long tube.

↓

In the tube, glucose, water, and other materials are reabsorbed.

↓

Urine flows from the kidneys through ureters to the urinary bladder.

LIFE SCIENCE

© Pearson Education, Inc.

SECTION 1 Infectious Disease

Key Ideas

◆ Infectious diseases are caused by pathogens: bacteria, viruses, fungi, and protists.
◆ Pathogens that infect humans can come from another person, a contaminated object, an animal bite, or the environment.

Key Terms

pathogen   infectious disease   toxin

SECTION 2 The Body's Defenses

Key Ideas

◆ The body has three lines of defense against pathogens.
◆ The immune system targets specific pathogens. T cells identify pathogens and distinguish one kind from another. B cells produce antibodies that destroy pathogens.
◆ HIV, the virus that causes AIDS, infects and destroys T cells.

Key Terms

inflammatory response	antigen
phagocyte B cell	
immune response	antibody
lymphocyte AIDS	
T cell	

SECTION 3 Preventing Infectious Disease

Key Ideas

◆ In active immunity, a person's own immune system produces antibodies. A person can acquire active immunity by having the disease or by being vaccinated.
◆ In passive immunity, the antibodies come from a source other than the person's body.

Key Terms

immunity	vaccination	passive
active	vaccine	immunity
immunity		antibiotic

SECTION 4 Noninfectious Disease

Key Ideas

◆ Noninfectious diseases are diseases that are not spread from person to person.
◆ An allergy is a disorder in which the immune system is overly sensitive to a foreign substance, called an allergen.
◆ In diabetes, the body does not produce enough insulin or can't use it properly.
◆ In cancer, cells multiply uncontrollably, destroying healthy tissues.

Key Terms

noninfectious disease	insulin
allergy	diabetes
allergen	tumor
histamine	carcinogen
asthma	

THE BODY'S REACTION TO TUBERCULOSIS BACTERIA IN THE LUNGS

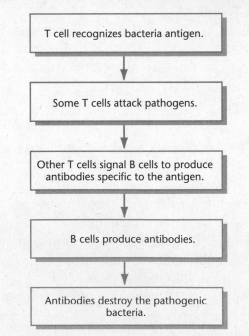

T cell recognizes bacteria antigen.

↓

Some T cells attack pathogens.

↓

Other T cells signal B cells to produce antibodies specific to the antigen.

↓

B cells produce antibodies.

↓

Antibodies destroy the pathogenic bacteria.

SECTION 1 How the Nervous System Works

Key Idea
◆ The nervous system receives information about the external and internal environment and helps maintain homeostasis.

Key Terms
stimulus	dendrite	interneuron
response	axon	motor neuron
neuron	nerve	synapse
nerve impulse	sensory neuron	

FUNCTIONS OF NERVE CELLS

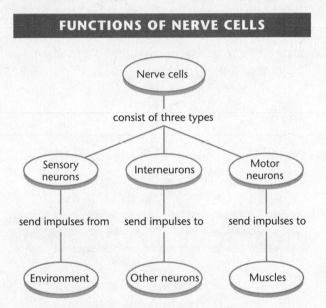

SECTION 2 Divisions of the Nervous System

Key Ideas
◆ The central nervous system consists of the brain and spinal cord.
◆ The peripheral nervous system links the central nervous system to the rest of the body.

Key Terms
central nervous system	brainstem
peripheral nervous system	somatic nervous system
brain	autonomic nervous system
spinal cord	
cerebrum	reflex
cerebellum	concussion

SECTION 3 The Senses

Key Ideas
◆ The senses change information about the environment to nerve impulses.
◆ After light enters the eye, it passes through the lens, which focuses it on the retina. Impulses then travel to the brain.
◆ Sound waves start vibrations in structures in the ear. When the vibrations reach the cochlea, impulses are sent to the brain.

Key Terms
cornea	retina	eardrum
pupil	nearsightedness	cochlea
iris	farsightedness	semicircular canal
lens		

SECTION 4 Alcohol and Other Drugs

Key Ideas
◆ Abused drugs act on the nervous system. Depressants slow down the central nervous system. Stimulants speed up body processes. Marijuana, alcohol, amphetamines, and anabolic steroids are commonly abused drugs.
◆ The long-term abuse of alcohol can damage the liver and brain and lead to alcoholism.

Key Terms
drug	withdrawal	anabolic steroid
drug abuse	depressant	alcoholism
tolerance	stimulant	

LIFE SCIENCE

Chapter 8   The Endocrine System & Reproduction

SECTION 1 — The Endocrine System

Key Ideas
◆ The endocrine system controls many of the body's daily activities, as well as the body's overall development.
◆ The endocrine system releases chemical messages called hormones. Hormones travel through the bloodstream to their target organs.
◆ Homeostasis in the body is maintained partly through negative feedback: the right amount of a particular hormone signals the body to stop producing that hormone.

Key Terms
endocrine gland   hypothalamus
hormone   pituitary gland
target cell   negative feedback

SECTION 2 — The Male and Female Reproductive Systems

Key Ideas
◆ The male reproductive system is specialized to produce sperm and the hormone testosterone.
◆ The role of the female reproductive system is to produce eggs and to nourish a developing baby until birth.
◆ Eggs are produced in the ovaries of the female. During the menstrual cycle, an egg develops, and the uterus prepares for the arrival of a fertilized egg.

Key Terms
egg   penis
sperm   ovary
fertilization   estrogen
reproduction   oviduct
zygote   uterus
chromosome   vagina
testis   menstrual cycle
testosterone   ovulation
scrotum   menstruation
semen

SECTION 3 — The Human Life Cycle

Key Ideas
◆ If an egg is fertilized, pregnancy begins. The zygote develops into an embryo and then a fetus.
◆ A fetus develops inside the mother's uterus for about 9 months before it is born. Birth takes place in three stages—labor, delivery, and afterbirth.
◆ Infancy is a time of rapid physical growth and mastery of basic skills. During childhood, children become more independent.
◆ Adolescence includes the physical changes of puberty as well as mental and social changes.
◆ Puberty is the period of sexual development in which the body becomes able to reproduce.

Key Terms
embryo   umbilical cord puberty
amniotic sac fetus   peer pressure
placenta   adolescence

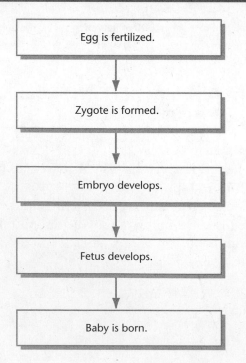

MAIN STAGES BETWEEN HUMAN FERTILIZATION AND BIRTH

Egg is fertilized.

↓

Zygote is formed.

↓

Embryo develops.

↓

Fetus develops.

↓

Baby is born.

TOPIC 5

ENVIRONMENTAL SCIENCE

SECTION 1   Living Things and the Environment

Key Ideas

◆ An organism's habitat provides food, water, shelter, and other things the organism needs to live, grow, and reproduce.

◆ An ecosystem includes both biotic and abiotic factors. Abiotic factors found in many environments include water, sunlight, oxygen, temperature, and soil.

◆ A population consists of a single species. The different populations living together in one area make up a community. The community plus abiotic factors form an ecosystem.

◆ Ecologists study how the biotic and abiotic factors interact within an ecosystem.

Key Terms

ecosystem	species
habitat	population
biotic factor	community
abiotic factor	ecology
photosynthesis	

SECTION 2   Studying Populations

Key Ideas

◆ Ecologists can estimate population size by direct and indirect observations, sampling, and mark-and-recapture studies.

◆ A population changes in size as a result of changes in the birth rate or death rate, or when organisms move into or out of the population.

◆ Population size is controlled by limiting factors such as food, space, and weather conditions.

Key Terms

population density	immigration
estimate	emigration
birth rate	limiting factor
death rate	carrying capacity

SECTION 3   Interactions Among Living Things

Key Ideas

◆ Over time, species of organisms develop specialized adaptations and behaviors that help them succeed in their environments.

◆ The major types of interactions among organisms are competition, predation, and symbiosis.

◆ Symbiosis is a close relationship between two species. The three types of symbiotic relationships are mutualism, commensalism, and parasitism.

Key Terms

natural selection	predator	commensalism
adaptation	prey	parasitism
niche	symbiosis	parasite
competition	mutualism	host
predation		

INTERACTIONS AMONG ORGANISMS

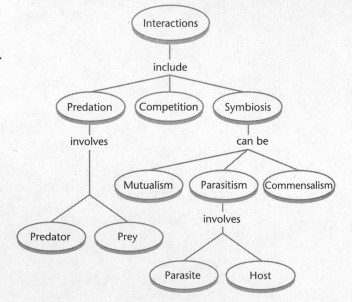

SECTION 1 Energy Flow in Ecosystems

Key Ideas

◆ The energy role of an organism is that of a producer, consumer, or decomposer.
◆ Producers are the source of all the food in an ecosystem.
◆ Consumers include herbivores, carnivores, omnivores, and scavengers.
◆ Decomposers return nutrients to the environment where they can be used again.
◆ A food web shows feeding relationships.
◆ At each level in an energy pyramid, there is less available energy than at the level below.

Key Terms

producer	omnivore	food web
consumer	scavenger	energy
herbivore	decomposer	pyramid
carnivore	food chain	

SECTION 2 Cycles of Matter

Key Ideas

◆ Matter cycles through an ecosystem. Energy must be supplied constantly.
◆ The processes of evaporation, condensation, and precipitation form the water cycle.

Key Terms

water cycle	condensation	nitrogen
evaporation	precipitation	fixation
		nodule

SECTION 3 Biogeography

Key Ideas

◆ Means of dispersal of organisms include continental drift, wind, water, and living things.
◆ Three factors that limit dispersal are physical barriers, competition, and climate.

Key Terms

biogeography	native species
continental drift	exotic species
dispersal	climate

SECTION 4 Earth's Biomes

Key Ideas

◆ Temperature and rainfall mostly determine the biome in an area. Land biomes include rain forests, deserts, grasslands, deciduous forests, boreal forests, and tundras.
◆ Photosynthesis occurs only near the surface or in shallow areas of water biomes.

Key Terms

biome	savanna	permafrost
canopy	deciduous tree	estuary
understory	hibernation	intertidal zone
desert	coniferous tree	neritic zone
grassland	tundra	

SECTION 5 Succession

Key Idea

◆ Primary succession occurs where no previous ecosystem exists. Secondary succession occurs after a disturbance.

Key Terms

succession	pioneer species
primary succession	secondary succession

HOW CARBON CYCLES THROUGH AN ECOSYSTEM

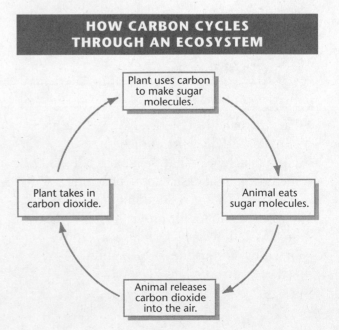

Skills and Content Review

Environmental Issues

Key Ideas

◆ Three types of environmental issues are resource use, population growth, and pollution.

◆ Making environmental decisions requires balancing different viewpoints and weighing the costs and benefits of proposals.

Key Terms

renewable resources
nonrenewable
  resources
pollution

development viewpoint
preservation viewpoint
conservation viewpoint

Forests and Fisheries

Key Ideas

◆ Because new trees can be planted to replace those that are cut down, forests can be renewable resources.

◆ Managing fisheries involves setting fishing limits, changing fishing methods, using aquaculture, and finding new resources.

Key Terms

clear-cutting
selective cutting
sustainable yield

fishery
aquaculture

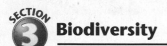

Biodiversity

Key Ideas

◆ Factors that affect biodiversity include area, climate, and diversity of niches.

◆ Human activities that threaten biodiversity include habitat destruction, poaching, pollution, and introduction of exotic species.

◆ Three techniques for protecting biodiversity are regulating capture and trade, captive breeding, and habitat preservation.

Key Terms

biodiversity
keystone species
genes
extinction
endangered species

threatened species
habitat destruction
habitat fragmentation
poaching
captive breeding

FACTS ABOUT BIODIVERSITY

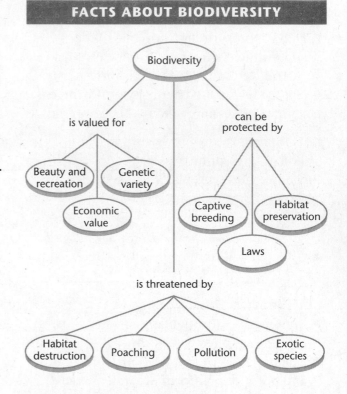

The Search for New Medicines

Key Ideas

◆ Many plants make chemicals that protect them from predators, parasites, and disease. These chemicals may fight human diseases.

◆ The cancer-fighting drug taxol comes from Pacific yew trees, which have been affected by logging of the forests where they grow.

◆ The possible discovery of other medicines is one reason to protect biodiversity.

Key Term

taxol

SECTION 1 How Land Is Used

Key Ideas

◆ Land is a nonrenewable resource. All the people on Earth must share this limited resource for agriculture, development, mining, and other uses.

◆ Soil is a complex system that takes a very long time to form.

◆ Poor soil management can cause erosion, nutrient depletion, and desertification.

◆ There are many farming techniques to help prevent erosion and nutrient depletion.

Key Terms

development	nutrient depletion
litter	fallow
topsoil	crop rotation
subsoil	desertification
bedrock	land reclamation
erosion	

SECTION 2 Solid Waste

Key Ideas

◆ Wastes are produced in the making and using of many products.

◆ Three ways of handling solid waste are to bury it, to burn it, or to recycle it.

◆ Most municipal solid waste in the United States is buried in sanitary landfills.

◆ The main types of municipal solid waste that are recycled are metal, glass, paper, and plastic.

◆ Recycling can conserve both resources and energy. However, there are not always many ways to use recycled materials.

◆ One way to help solve the solid waste problem is to practice the "three R's"— reduce, reuse, and recycle.

Key Terms

municipal solid waste	recycling
leachate	biodegradable
sanitary landfill	resins
incineration	composting

SECTION 3 Hazardous Wastes

Key Ideas

◆ Hazardous wastes are materials that can threaten human health and safety or can be harmful to the environment if they are not properly disposed of.

◆ Hazardous wastes include toxic, explosive, flammable, and corrosive wastes. Radioactive wastes also require special disposal.

◆ How a person is affected by a hazardous substance depends on several factors, including the amount of the substance, the length of time the person is exposed, and how the substance enters the person's body.

◆ It is very difficult to find safe ways to dispose of hazardous wastes and good places to store them. A good way to manage hazardous wastes is to produce less of them.

Key Terms

hazardous waste	flammable
toxic	corrosive
explosive	radioactive

LANDFILLS VERSUS INCINERATORS

	Landfill	Incinerator
Cost	Cheaper to build, more expensive to operate	More expensive to build, cheaper to operate
Pollution	Can pollute soil and groundwater	Can pollute air; create solid waste that must be disposed of elsewhere
Attractiveness	Unattractive	More attractive than landfill
Usefulness to Community	Provide jobs; produce methane that can be used as fuel	Provide jobs; generate electricity

SECTION 1 Air Pollution

Key Ideas

◆ Air pollutants can be in the form of solid particles or gases.

◆ The major sources of photochemical smog are the gases emitted by motor vehicles.

◆ Sources of indoor air pollution include smoke, dust, pet hair, asbestos, and other substances. Two dangerous pollutants that are very difficult to detect are carbon monoxide and radon.

◆ Certain gases in Earth's atmosphere prevent heat from escaping back into space.

◆ The ozone layer protects people and other living things from the effects of too much ultraviolet radiation.

◆ Most scientists base their climate predictions on computer models that calculate the effects of changes in the atmosphere.

Key Terms

air pollution	acid rain
emissions	ozone layer
photochemical smog	chlorofluorocarbons
ozone	greenhouse effect
temperature inversion	global warming

AIR POLLUTION

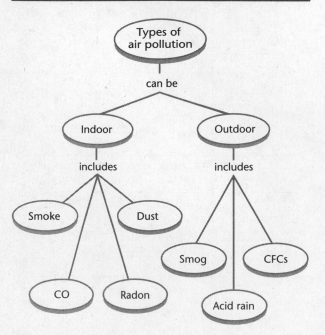

SECTION 2 The Water Supply

Key Ideas

◆ Most of Earth's water—about 97 percent—is salt water.

◆ People and many other organisms require fresh water to carry out their life processes.

◆ Although there are some natural sources of water pollution, most pollution is the result of human activities. Agriculture, industry, construction, and mining all produce wastes that can end up in water.

Key Terms

groundwater	fertilizer
drought	pesticide
water pollution	sediments
sewage	

SECTION 3 Finding Pollution Solutions

Key Ideas

◆ The major role of technology in controlling air pollution is to reduce emissions.

◆ Two basic ways to reduce water pollution are to treat wastes so that they are less harmful, and to find substitutes for pollutants.

Key Terms

scrubber	primary treatment
catalytic converter	secondary treatment

SECTION 1   Fossil Fuels

Key Ideas

◆ A fuel is a substance that provides a form of energy as a result of a chemical change.

◆ Energy can be converted from one form to another.

◆ The three major fossil fuels are coal, oil, and natural gas. They release more energy when burned than most other substances do.

◆ Because fossil fuels take hundreds of millions of years to form, they are considered nonrenewable resources.

Key Terms

combustion   petroleum
fossil fuels   refinery
hydrocarbons   petrochemicals
reserves

SECTION 2   Renewable Sources of Energy

Key Ideas

◆ Solar energy is plentiful and renewable, and does not cause pollution. However, a backup energy source is needed.

◆ Because the sun causes winds and drives the water cycle, wind power and water power are considered indirect forms of solar energy.

◆ Biomass fuels, geothermal energy, and hydrogen power are other renewable energy sources that are currently in limited use.

Key Terms

solar energy   biomass fuels
passive solar system   gasohol
active solar system   geothermal energy
hydroelectric power

SECTION 3   Nuclear Energy

Key Ideas

◆ Nuclear reactions include fission reactions and fusion reactions.

◆ In a fission reaction, an atom's nucleus is split into two smaller nuclei and two or more neutrons, releasing energy.

◆ In a nuclear power plant, the thermal energy released from controlled fission reactions is used to generate electricity.

Key Terms

nucleus   fuel rods   meltdown
nuclear fission   control rods   nuclear fusion
reactor vessel

SECTION 4   Energy Conservation

Key Ideas

◆ To avoid an energy shortage in the future, people must find new energy sources and conserve available fuels now.

◆ Insulation keeps a building from losing heat to, or gaining heat from, the outside.

Key Terms

energy conservation   efficiency   insulation

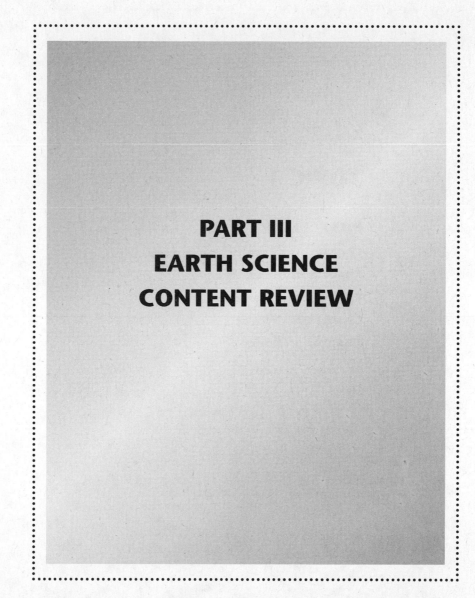

PART III
EARTH SCIENCE
CONTENT REVIEW

TOPIC 1

INSIDE EARTH

SECTION 1 — Earth's Interior

Key Ideas

◆ Earth's interior is divided into the crust, the mantle, the outer core, and the inner core.

◆ The lithosphere includes the crust and the rigid upper layer of the mantle; beneath the lithosphere lies the asthenosphere.

Key Terms

geologist	seismic wave	lithosphere
rock	pressure	asthenospere
geology	crust	outer core
constructive force	basalt	inner core
destructive force	granite	
continent	mantle	

SECTION 2 — Convection Currents and the Mantle

Key Ideas

◆ Heat can be transferred in three ways: radiation, conduction, and convection.

◆ Differences of temperature and density within a fluid cause convection currents.

Key Terms

heat transfer	convection
radiation	density
conduction	convection current

SECTION 3 — Drifting Continents

Key Ideas

◆ Alfred Wegener developed the idea that the continents were once joined and have since drifted apart.

◆ Most scientists rejected Wegener's theory because he could not identify a force that could move the continents.

Key Terms

Pangaea	fossil
continental drift	

SECTION 4 — Sea-Floor Spreading

Key Ideas

◆ In sea-floor spreading, molten material forms new rock along the mid-ocean ridge.

◆ In subduction, the ocean floor sinks back to the mantle beneath deep ocean trenches.

Key Terms

mid-ocean ridge	deep-ocean trench
sonar	subduction
sea-floor spreading	

CYCLE OF SUBDUCTION AND ERUPTION

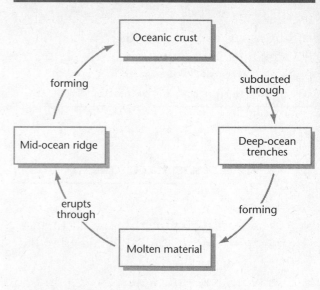

SECTION 5 — The Theory of Plate Tectonics

Key Idea

◆ Plates slip past each other at transform boundaries, move apart at divergent boundaries, and come together at convergent boundaries.

Key Terms

plate	transform boundary
scientific theory	divergent boundary
plate tectonics	rift valley
fault	convergent boundary

SECTION 1 ## Earth's Crust in Motion

Key Ideas
◆ Stresses on Earth's crust produce compression, tension, and shearing in rock.
◆ Faults are cracks in Earth's crust that result from stress.
◆ Faulting and folding of the crust cause mountains and other features to form on the surface.

Key Terms
earthquake	hanging wall
stress	footwall
shearing	reverse fault
tension	fault-block mountain
compression	folds
deformation	anticline
fault	syncline
strike-slip fault	plateau
normal fault	

SECTION 2 ## Measuring Earthquakes

Key Ideas
◆ As seismic waves travel through Earth, they carry the energy of an earthquake from the focus to the surface.
◆ Two types of seismic waves, P waves and S waves, travel out in all directions from the focus of an earthquake.
◆ Today, the moment magnitude scale is used to determine the magnitude of an earthquake. Other scales include the Mercalli scale and the Richter scale.

Key Terms
focus	seismograph
epicenter	magnitude
seismic waves	Mercalli scale
P waves	Richter scale
S waves	moment magnitude scale
surface waves	

SECTION 3 ## Earthquake Hazards and Safety

Key Ideas
◆ Earthquakes can damage structures through tsunamis, landslides or avalanches, and shaking or liquefaction of the ground.
◆ New buildings can be designed to withstand earthquakes; old buildings can be modified to make them more earthquake-resistant.
◆ For personal safety indoors during an earthquake, drop, cover, and hold under a desk or table, or against an interior wall.

Key Terms
liquefaction	tsunamis
aftershock	base-isolated building

SECTION 4 ## Monitoring Faults

Key Ideas
◆ Geologists use instruments to measure deformation and stress along faults.
◆ Scientists determine earthquake risk by monitoring active faults and by studying faults where past earthquakes have occurred.

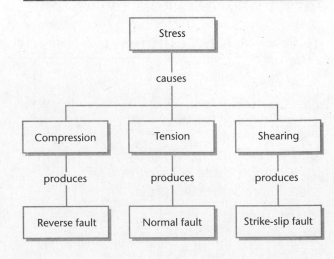

STRESS FORCES IN EARTH'S CRUST

SECTION 1 ## Volcanoes and Plate Tectonics

Key Ideas

◆ A volcano is an opening on Earth's surface where magma escapes from the interior. Magma that reaches Earth's surface is called lava.

◆ The constructive force of volcanoes adds new rock to existing land and forms new islands.

◆ Most volcanoes occur near the boundaries of Earth's plates and along the edges of continents, in island arcs, or along mid-ocean ridges.

Key Terms

volcano	lava	island arc
magma	Ring of Fire	hot spot

SECTION 2 ## Volcanic Activity

Key Ideas

◆ An eruption occurs when gases trapped in magma rush through an opening at the Earth's surface, carrying magma with them.

◆ Volcanoes can erupt quietly or explosively, depending on the amount of dissolved gases in the magma and on how thick or runny the magma is.

◆ When magma heats water underground, hot springs and geysers form.

◆ Volcano hazards include pyroclastic flows, avalanches of mud, damage from ash, lava flows, flooding, and deadly gases.

Key Terms

magma chamber	pyroclastic flow
pipe	active
vent	dormant
lava flow	extinct
crater	hot spring
silica	geyser
pahoehoe	geothermal energy
aa	

 SECTION 3 ## Volcanic Landforms

Key Ideas

◆ Lava and other volcanic materials on the surface create shield volcanoes, cinder cones, composite volcanoes, and plateaus.

◆ Magma that hardens beneath the surface creates batholiths, dome mountains, dikes, and sills, which are eventually exposed when the covering rock wears away.

Key Terms

shield volcano	caldera	sill
cinder cone	volcanic neck	batholith
composite volcano	dike	

CHARACTERISTICS OF VOLCANIC MOUNTAINS

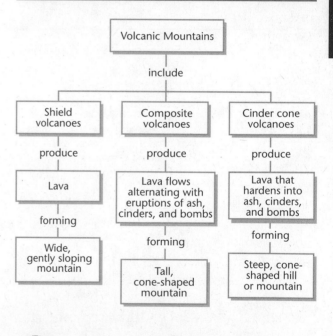

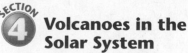 **SECTION 4** ## Volcanoes in the Solar System

Key Ideas

◆ Venus and Mars both have extinct volcanoes similar to volcanoes on Earth.

◆ Spacecraft have photographed volcanic activity on moons of Jupiter and Neptune.

EARTH SCIENCE

EARTH SCIENCE

SECTION 1 — Properties of Minerals

Key Ideas

◆ A mineral is a naturally occurring inorganic solid that has a distinct chemical composition and crystal shape.

◆ Each mineral can be identified by its own physical and chemical properties.

◆ Some of the properties of minerals include hardness, color, streak, luster, density, cleavage and fracture, and crystal structure. Hardness is measured by the Mohs hardness scale.

◆ Minerals usually consist of two or more elements joined together in a compound.

Key Terms

mineral	Mohs hardness scale
inorganic	streak
crystal	luster
element	cleavage
compound	fracture
	fluorescence

COMPARING HEMATITE AND BRICK

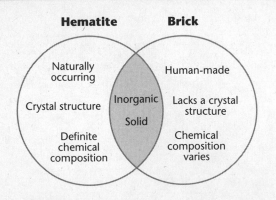

Hematite: Naturally occurring, Crystal structure, Definite chemical composition

Inorganic Solid

Brick: Human-made, Lacks a crystal structure, Chemical composition varies

SECTION 2 — How Minerals Form

Key Ideas

◆ Minerals form inside Earth through crystallization as magma or lava cools.

◆ Minerals form on Earth's surface when materials dissolved in water crystallize through evaporation.

◆ Mineral deposits form on the ocean floor from solutions heated by magma. The hot-water solutions containing minerals erupt through chimneys on the ocean floor, then crystallize when they come in contact with cold sea water.

Key Terms

solution   vein

SECTION 3 — Mineral Resources

Key Ideas

◆ Minerals are useful as the source of all metals, gemstones, and of many other materials.

◆ Geologists locate ore deposits by prospecting—looking for certain features on and beneath Earth's surface.

◆ Ores can be removed from the ground through open pit mines, strip mines, or shaft mines.

◆ Smelting is the process of heating an ore to extract a metal.

Key Terms

gemstone	smelting
ore	alloy

SECTION 1 Classifying Rocks

Key Ideas

◆ A rock is a hard piece of Earth's crust.
◆ Geologists classify rocks according to their color, texture, mineral composition, and origin.
◆ The three kinds of rocks are igneous, sedimentary, and metamorphic.

Key Terms

texture   igneous rock   metamorphic rock
grain   sedimentary rock

SECTION 2 Igneous Rocks

Key Ideas

◆ Igneous rocks form from magma or lava.
◆ Igneous rocks are classified according to their origin, texture, and composition.

Key Terms

extrusive rock   intrusive rock   porphyritic
                                   texture

SECTION 3 Sedimentary Rocks

Key Ideas

◆ Most sedimentary rocks form from sediments that are compacted and cemented together.
◆ The three types of sedimentary rocks are clastic rocks, organic rocks, and chemical rocks.

Key Terms

sediment   compaction   organic rock
erosion   cementation   chemical rock
deposition   clastic rock

SECTION 4 Rocks from Reefs

Key Idea

◆ When corals die, their skeletons remain. More corals grow on top of them, slowly forming a reef.

Key Terms

coral reef   atoll

SECTION 5 Metamorphic Rocks

Key Ideas

◆ In a process that takes place deep beneath the surface, heat and pressure can change any type of rock into metamorphic rock.
◆ Geologists classify metamorphic rock according to whether the rock is foliated or nonfoliated.

Key Term

foliated

SECTION 6 The Rock Cycle

Key Idea

◆ The series of processes on and beneath Earth's surface that change rocks from one type of rock to another is called the rock cycle.

Key Term

rock cycle

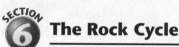

STEPS IN THE ROCK CYCLE

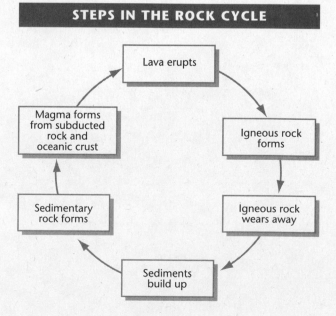

EARTH SCIENCE

Skills and Content Review   **79**

TOPIC 2

EARTH'S CHANGING SURFACE

SECTION 1   Exploring Earth's Surface

Key Ideas

◆ Earth's topography is made up of landforms that have elevation and relief, such as plains, mountains, and plateaus.

◆ The atmosphere, hydrosphere, and biosphere surround Earth's rocky outer layer, the lithosphere.

Key Terms

topography	landform	plateau
elevation	region	lithosphere
relief	plain	atmosphere
landform	mountain	hydrosphere
	mountain range	biosphere

TYPES OF LANDFORMS

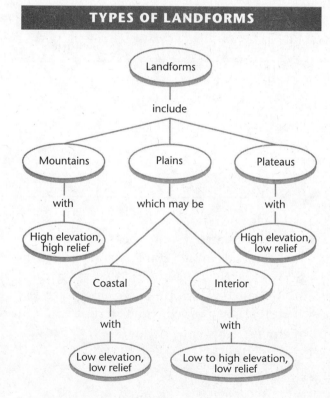

SECTION 2   Mapping Earth's Surface

Key Ideas

◆ Maps and globes are drawn to scale to show features on Earth's surface as seen from above.

◆ The grid of latitude and longitude lines can be used to locate points on Earth's surface.

Key Terms

map	key	degree
globe	equator	latitude
scale	hemisphere	longitude
symbols	prime meridian	map projection

SECTION 3   Maps in the Computer Age

Key Ideas

◆ Instruments carried aboard satellites in orbit around Earth make pictures of the surface called satellite images.

◆ Computers are used to store and display the information used in making maps.

Key Terms

satellite image	digitizing
pixel	

SECTION 4   Topographic Maps

Key Ideas

◆ Topographic maps portray the elevation, relief, and slope of the landforms in an area.

◆ Contour lines are used on a topographic map to show elevation and relief.

◆ The contour interval of a topographic map is the amount that elevation increases or decreases between contour lines.

◆ In addition to showing elevation and relief, topographic maps include a variety of other natural and human-made features.

Key Terms

topographic map	contour interval
contour line	Global Positioning System

EARTH SCIENCE

SECTION 1 Rocks and Weathering

Key Ideas

◆ Rock weathers, or wears down, when it is exposed to air, water, weather, and living things at Earth's surface.

◆ Mechanical weathering breaks rock into smaller pieces. The agents of mechanical weathering include freezing and thawing, release of pressure, growth of plants, actions of animals, and abrasion.

◆ Chemical weathering changes the mineral content of rock. The agents of chemical weathering are water, oxygen, carbon dioxide, living organisms, and acid rain.

◆ Climate and rock type determine how fast weathering occurs.

Key Terms

weathering   ice wedging
erosion   chemical weathering
mechanical weathering   permeable
abrasion

SECTION 2 Soil Formation and Composition

Key Ideas

◆ Soil is made of small particles of rock mixed with the decaying remains of organisms.

◆ Soil forms in layers called horizons as bedrock weathers and organic materials build up.

◆ The three soil horizons are the A horizon, the B horizon, and the C horizon. The A horizon is made up of topsoil, which is rich in humus. The B horizon consists of clay and other particles washed down from the A horizon, but little humus. The C horizon is made up of partly weathered rock without clay or humus.

◆ Plants and animals break up and mix the soil, and also add the organic materials that form humus.

Key Terms

soil   loam   subsoil
bedrock   soil horizon   litter
humus   topsoil   decomposers

SOIL HORIZONS

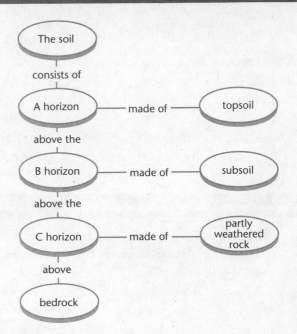

SECTION 3 Soil Conservation

Key Ideas

◆ Soil is a valuable resource because life on land depends on it, yet it forms very slowly.

◆ Soil can be eroded away and its fertility can be decreased by improper farming practices.

◆ Soil can be conserved and its fertility can be maintained by using various methods of soil conservation.

Key Terms

sod   contour plowing
Dust Bowl   conservation plowing
soil conservation

EARTH SCIENCE

SECTION 1 — Changing Earth's Surface

Key Ideas
◆ Weathering, erosion, and deposition act to wear down and build up Earth's surface.
◆ Gravity pulls sediment downhill in the process of mass movement. There are four main types of mass movement: landslides, mudslides, slump, and creep.

Key Terms
erosion   deposition
sediment   mass movement

SECTION 2 — Water Erosion

Key Ideas
◆ Moving water is the major force of erosion that has shaped Earth's land surface.
◆ A river may form V-shaped valleys, waterfalls, meanders, oxbow lakes, and flood plains.
◆ When a river slows down, it deposits some of the sediment load it carries, forming features such as alluvial fans and deltas.

Key Terms
runoff	drainage basin	delta
rill	divide	groundwater
gully	flood plain	stalactite
stream	meander	stalagmite
river	oxbow lake	karst topography
tributary	alluvial fan	

SECTION 3 — The Force of Moving Water

Key Ideas
◆ When gravity pulls water down a slope, water's potential energy changes to kinetic energy, and it does work.
◆ Most sediment washes or falls into streams, or is eroded from the streambed by abrasion.
◆ The greater a river's slope or volume of flow, the more sediment it can erode.

Key Terms
energy   abrasion   friction
potential energy load   turbulence
kinetic energy

SECTION 4 — Glaciers

Key Idea
◆ Glaciers erode the land through plucking and abrasion. Melting glaciers deposit sediment.

Key Terms
glacier	ice age	moraine
valley glacier	plucking	kettle
continental glacier	till	

SECTION 5 — Waves

Key Ideas
◆ The energy of ocean waves comes from wind blowing across the water's surface and transferring energy to the water.
◆ Ocean waves hitting land cause erosion through impact and abrasion. Waves also move and deposit sediment along the shore.

Key Terms
beach   longshore drift   spit

SECTION 6 — Wind Erosion

Key Ideas
◆ Wind causes erosion mainly through deflation, the blowing of surface materials.
◆ Landforms created by wind deposition include sand dunes and loess deposits.

Key Terms
sand dune   deflation   loess

EARTH SCIENCE

EARTH SCIENCE

1 Fossils

Key Ideas
◆ Most fossils form when living things die and are quickly buried by sediment, which eventually hardens and preserves parts of the organisms.
◆ The major kinds of fossils include petrified remains, molds, casts, carbon films, trace fossils, and preserved remains.
◆ The fossil record shows that many different organisms have lived on Earth at different times and that groups of organisms have changed over time.

Key Terms
fossil	mold	scientific
paleontologist	cast	theory
sedimentary rock	carbon film	evolution
petrified fossil	trace fossil	extinct

2 Finding the Relative Age of Rocks

Key Ideas
◆ The law of superposition can be used to determine the relative ages of rock layers.
◆ Scientists also study faults, intrusions, and extrusions to find the relative ages of rock layers.
◆ Index fossils are useful in dating rock layers.

Key Terms
relative age	fault
absolute age	intrusion
law of superposition	extrusion
unconformity	index fossil

3 Radioactive Dating

Key Ideas
◆ During radioactive decay, the atoms of one element decay into atoms of another element.
◆ Scientists use radioactive dating to determine the absolute ages of rocks.

Key Terms
atom	radioactive decay
element	half-life

4 The Geologic Time Scale

Key Idea
◆ The basic divisions of the geologic time scale are eras, periods, and epochs.

Key Terms
geologic time scale	invertebrate	epoch
era	period	

5 Earth's History

Key Ideas
◆ A great number of different kinds of living things evolved during the "Cambrian explosion" at the beginning of the Paleozoic Era.
◆ During the Permian Period, the continents joined to form the supercontinent Pangaea.

Key Terms
vertebrate	reptile	mammal
amphibian	mass extinction	

TOPIC 3

EARTH'S WATERS

EARTH SCIENCE

SECTION 1 How Is Water Important?

Key Ideas

◆ People use water for many purposes, including household use, industry, agriculture, transportation, and recreation.

◆ All living things need water to carry out their life processes.

◆ About 97 percent of Earth's water is salt water stored in the oceans. Less than 1 percent is usable fresh water.

Key Terms

irrigation   habitat   groundwater
photosynthesis   water vapor

SECTION 2 The Properties of Water

Key Ideas

◆ A water molecule consists of two hydrogen atoms bonded to an oxygen atom. The hydrogen ends of the molecule have a slight positive charge. The oxygen end of the molecule has a slight negative charge.

◆ The charged ends of water's polar molecules attract the charged ends of other water molecules. Water molecules are also attracted to other charged particles.

◆ Some properties caused by the attractions among water molecules are surface tension, capillary action, and high specific heat.

◆ Water dissolves so many substances that it is sometimes called the "universal solvent."

◆ Water on Earth exists in three states: liquid water; ice, a solid; and water vapor, a gas.

◆ Energy must be added or released for water molecules to change state.

◆ Unlike most other substances, the solid form of water is less dense than the liquid form.

Key Terms

polar molecule   solution   evaporation
surface tension   solvent   condensation
capillary action   state   specific heat

SECTION 3 The Water Cycle

Key Ideas

◆ In the water cycle, water evaporates from Earth's surface into the atmosphere. The water forms clouds, then falls back to Earth as precipitation. The sun's energy drives the water cycle.

◆ The water cycle renews Earth's supply of fresh water. In the world as a whole, the rates of evaporation and precipitation balance each other.

Key Terms

water cycle   transpiration   precipitation

PATH OF A WATER MOLECULE

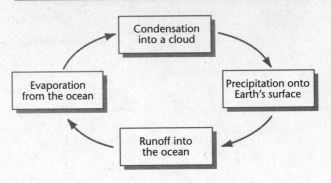

EARTH SCIENCE

SECTION 1 Streams and Rivers

Key Ideas

◆ Runoff from precipitation forms streams, which flow together to form rivers.

◆ Rivers wear away landforms through erosion and build new ones through deposition.

Key Terms

runoff	deposition	oxbow lake
tributary	sediment	mouth
watershed	headwaters	delta
divide	flood plain	levee
erosion	meander	

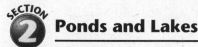

SECTION 2 Ponds and Lakes

Key Ideas

◆ Ponds and lakes are bodies of standing water that form when fresh water collects in depressions in the land.

◆ Lake turnover is a seasonal mixing that refreshes the nutrient supply in the lake.

Key Terms

reservoir   eutrophication

SECTION 3 Wetland Environments

Key Idea

◆ Wetlands provide nesting and feeding areas for birds and other wildlife. Wetlands also filter water and help control floods.

Key Term

wetland

WETLANDS

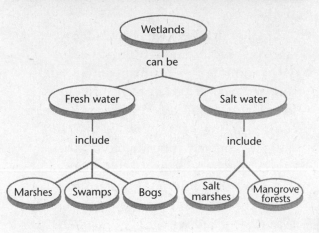

EARTH SCIENCE

SECTION 4 Glaciers and Icebergs

Key Ideas

◆ Glaciers form when layers of snow pile up.

◆ Icebergs form when the edges of glaciers reach the ocean and break off.

Key Term

glacier

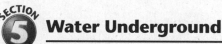

SECTION 5 Water Underground

Key Ideas

◆ As water soaks into the ground, it moves through the pores between particles of soil and rock. Water moves easily through permeable materials, but does not move easily through impermeable materials.

◆ People dig wells to obtain groundwater from aquifers. To supply water, a well must reach below the level of the water table.

◆ Water pressure brings groundwater to the surface naturally in artesian wells, springs, and geysers.

Key Terms

pore	unsaturated	artesian well
permeable	zone	spring
impermeable	water table	geyser
saturated	aquifer	
zone	recharge	

© Pearson Education, Inc.

SECTION 1 Water to Drink

Key Ideas
◆ Sources of drinking water include rivers, lakes, reservoirs, and groundwater.
◆ Many communities maintain public water supplies to collect, treat, and distribute water to residents. Some homes have private wells.
◆ Most drinking water is treated to ensure that it is safe and appealing to drink.
◆ Pumps and gravity are used to increase water pressure and move water through a system of pipes.
◆ Wastewater and sewage are treated to prevent contamination of drinking water.

Key Terms
water quality   filtration   sludge
pH   flocs   septic tank
hardness   coagulation   leach field
concentration   sewage

SECTION 2 Balancing Water Needs

Key Ideas
◆ Water is scarce in many places, leading to competition for limited supplies.
◆ Water shortage can occur when there is too little water or too much demand in an area.
◆ Industries can conserve water by reducing water use, recycling water, and reusing water.
◆ Desalination of ocean water and icebergs are two possible future sources of fresh water.

Key Terms
drought   conservation   desalination

SECTION 3 Freshwater Pollution

Key Ideas
◆ Sources of water pollution include human and animal wastes, industrial and agricultural chemicals, and runoff from roads.
◆ Acid rain is caused by sulfur and nitrogen from smokestacks and car exhausts.

Key Terms
water pollution   nonpoint source   pesticide
point source   acid rain

SOURCES OF FRESHWATER POLLUTION

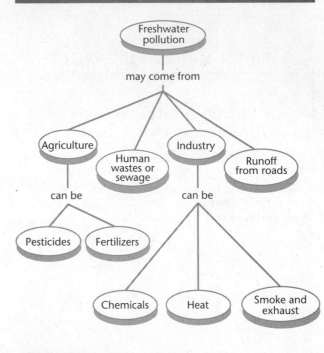

SECTION 4 Water as an Energy Resource

Key Idea
◆ Hydroelectric power plants capture the kinetic energy of moving water and change it into electrical energy.

Key Terms
kinetic energy   hydroelectric power
potential energy

© Pearson Education, Inc.

EARTH SCIENCE

SECTION 1 Wave Action

Key Ideas
◆ Most waves are caused by winds blowing across the surface of the water.
◆ When waves enter shallow water, the wavelength shortens and wave height increases.
◆ Waves erode shorelines, carving cliffs and breaking up rocks into pebbles and sand.

Key Terms
wave	trough	rip current
crest	wave height	groin
wavelength	longshore drift	tsunami
frequency	sandbar	

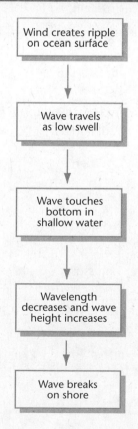

MOVEMENT OF A WAVE

Wind creates ripple on ocean surface

↓

Wave travels as low swell

↓

Wave touches bottom in shallow water

↓

Wavelength decreases and wave height increases

↓

Wave breaks on shore

SECTION 2 Tides

Key Ideas
◆ Tides are caused by the interaction of Earth, the moon, and the sun.
◆ There are two high tides and two low tides each day in most places.
◆ The height of tides during a month varies with changes in the positions of Earth, the moon, and the sun.

Key Terms
tide	spring tide	neap tide

SECTION 3 Ocean Water Chemistry

Key Ideas
◆ Chloride and sodium are the most abundant ions in ocean water.
◆ Salinity varies throughout the ocean.
◆ Below the ocean surface, the water is divided into layers by temperature, with uniformly cold temperatures in deep water.
◆ Pressure increases greatly with increasing depth in the ocean.

Key Terms
salinity	submersible

SECTION 4 Currents and Climate

Key Ideas
◆ Currents are formed by Earth's rotation, winds, and differences in water temperature.
◆ The movement of warm-water and cold-water surface currents carries water around the world and influences coastal climates.
◆ Density differences between warm and cold water cause many deep-water currents in the ocean.
◆ El Niño changes the pattern of winds and currents and affects Earth's weather.

Key Terms
current	climate	El Niño
Coriolis effect	upwelling	

EARTH SCIENCE

EARTH SCIENCE

SECTION 1   Exploring the Ocean

Key Ideas

◆ Technology such as sonar enables scientists to study the deep ocean floor despite the darkness, cold, and extreme pressure there.

◆ The ocean floor has features similar to those found on the continents, including plains, mountain ranges, volcanoes, and trenches.

Key Terms

sonar	mid-ocean ridge
continental shelf	trench
continental slope	magma
seamount	plates
abyssal plain	sea-floor spreading

SECTION 2   Life at the Ocean's Edge

Key Ideas

◆ Physical factors that affect marine organisms include water temperature, salinity, light, dissolved gases, nutrients, and wave action.

◆ Organisms in rocky intertidal zones must tolerate pounding from waves, and being both under water and exposed to air for long periods.

◆ Coastal wetlands include salt marshes and mangrove forests.

Key Terms

plankton	food web	estuary
nekton	intertidal zone	brackish
benthos		

SECTION 3   The Neritic Zone and Open Ocean

Key Ideas

◆ The neritic zone receives sunlight and nutrients washed from the land. Habitats in this zone include kelp forests and coral reefs.

◆ Chemical nutrients in hot water around a hydrothermal vent support organisms.

Key Terms

neritic zone	atoll
open-ocean zone	bioluminescence
holdfast	hydrothermal vent

OCEAN HABITATS		
Habitat/Zone	**Conditions**	**Organisms**
Tide pool/ Intertidal	Varying salinity, exposure, temperature, rough wave action	Barnacles, mussels, sea stars, sea urchins, sponges, sea anemones
Coral reef/ Neritic zone	Shallow water, warm temperatures, receives sunlight and a steady supply of nutrients, may have upwelling currents	Coral, fishes, shrimp, eels
Surface zone/ Open ocean	Receives sunlight, dissolved nutrients less abundant than in the neritic zone	Microscopic algae, copepods, krill, young of many ocean animals, jellyfish
Hydrothermal vent/ Deep zone	High pressure, dark, warm	Crabs, clams, tube worms, bacteria

SECTION 4   Resources From the Ocean

Key Ideas

◆ If used wisely, fisheries are a renewable resource.

◆ Nonliving resources from the ocean include dissolved substances in seawater and minerals and fuels from the ocean floor.

Key Terms

aquaculture	nodules

TOPIC 4

WEATHER AND CLIMATE

EARTH SCIENCE

EARTH SCIENCE

SECTION 1 The Air Around You

Key Ideas

Earth's atmosphere makes conditions on Earth suitable for living things.

Earth's atmosphere is made up of molecules of nitrogen, oxygen, carbon dioxide, and water vapor, as well as some other gases and particles of liquids and solids.

Key Terms

weather   ozone
atmosphere   water vapor

SECTION 2 Air Quality

Key Ideas

Most air pollution results from the burning of fossil fuels such as coal and oil.

Nitrogen oxides, hydrocarbons, and other air pollutants react with one another in the presence of sunlight to form a mix of ozone and other chemicals called photochemical smog.

Acid rain forms when nitrogen oxides and sulfur oxides combine with water in the air to form nitric acid and sulfuric acid.

Key Terms

pollutant   acid rain
photochemical smog

SECTION 3 Air Pressure

Key Ideas

◆ Properties of air include mass, density, and pressure.

Air pressure is the result of the weight of a column of air pushing down on an area.

Air pressure is measured with mercury barometers and aneroid barometers.

◆ Air pressure decreases as altitude increases. As air pressure decreases, so does density.

Key Terms

density   barometer   altitude
pressure   mercury barometer
air pressure   aneroid barometer

AIR PRESSURE

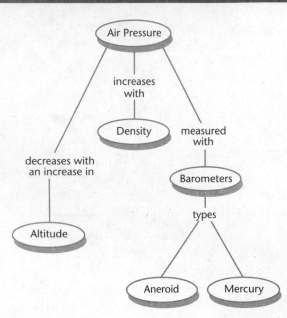

SECTION 4 Layers of the Atmosphere

Key Ideas

◆ The four main layers of the atmosphere are classified by changes in temperature.

◆ Rain, snow, storms, and most clouds occur in the troposphere.

◆ Ozone in the stratosphere absorbs energy from the sun.

◆ Most meteoroids burn up in the mesosphere, producing meteor trails.

◆ The aurora borealis occurs in the ionosphere.

◆ Communications satellites orbit Earth in the exosphere.

Key Terms

troposphere   thermosphere   aurora borealis
stratosphere   ionosphere   exosphere
mesosphere

© Pearson Education, Inc.

SECTION 1 — Energy in the Atmosphere

Key Ideas
◆ Energy from the sun travels to Earth as electromagnetic waves—mostly visible light, infrared radiation, and ultraviolet radiation.
◆ When Earth's surface is heated, it radiates some energy back into the atmosphere in the form of longer-wavelength radiation.

Key Terms
electromagnetic waves
radiation
infrared radiation
ultraviolet radiation
scattering
greenhouse effect

SECTION 2 — Heat Transfer

Key Ideas
◆ The energy of motion in the molecules of a substance is called thermal energy.
◆ Radiation, conduction, and convection work together to heat the troposphere.

Key Terms
thermal energy
temperature
thermometer
heat
conduction
convection

SECTION 3 — Winds

Key Ideas
◆ All winds are caused by differences in air pressure, which are the result of unequal heating of Earth's surface.
◆ Local winds are caused by unequal heating of Earth's surface within a small area.
◆ The movement of air between the equator and the poles produces global winds.

Key Terms
wind
anemometer
wind-chill factor
local wind
sea breeze
land breeze
monsoon
global wind
Coriolis effect
latitude
jet stream

EARTH'S WINDS

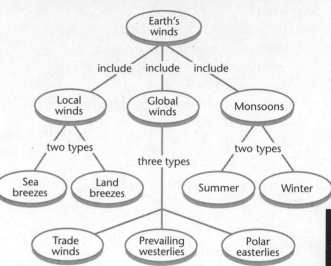

SECTION 4 — Water in the Atmosphere

Key Ideas
◆ Relative humidity is the percentage of water vapor in the air compared to the amount of water vapor the air could hold. It can be measured with a psychrometer.
◆ Clouds of all kinds form when water vapor in the air becomes liquid water or solid ice.
◆ Meteorologists classify clouds into three main types: cumulus, stratus, and cirrus.

Key Terms
evaporation
humidity
relative humidity
psychrometer
condensation
dew point
cumulus
stratus
cirrus

SECTION 5 — Precipitation

Key Ideas
◆ Common types of precipitation include rain, sleet, freezing rain, hail, and snow.
◆ Rain is measured with a rain gauge.
◆ Scientists have used cloud seeding to produce rain and to clear fog from airports.

Key Terms
precipitation
rain gauge
drought

EARTH SCIENCE

© Pearson Education, Inc.

SECTION 1 · Air Masses and Fronts

Key Ideas

◆ Four major types of air masses influence the weather in North America: maritime tropical, continental tropical, maritime polar, and continental polar.

◆ When air masses collide, they form four types of fronts: cold fronts, warm fronts, stationary fronts, and occluded fronts.

◆ Cyclones and decreasing air pressure are associated with storms and precipitation.

Key Terms

air mass	maritime	occluded
tropical	continental	cyclone
polar	front	anticyclone

EARTH SCIENCE

SECTION 2 · Storms

Key Ideas

◆ Thunderstorms and tornadoes form within large cumulonimbus clouds. During thunderstorms, avoid touching metal objects.

◆ A hurricane begins over warm water as a low-pressure area. If you hear a hurricane warning and are told to evacuate, leave the area immediately.

◆ Snow falls when humid air cools below 0°C. If you are caught in a snowstorm, try to find shelter from the wind.

Key Terms

storm	tornado	storm surge
lightning	hurricane	evacuate

HURRICANES vs. TORNADOES

Type of Storm	Hurricane	Tornado
Where storm forms	Over warm ocean water	In cumulonimbus clouds
Size of storm	Around 600 kilometers	Several hundred meters
How long storm lasts	A week or more	15 minutes or less
Time of year	Summer, early fall	Spring, early summer
Safety rules	Evacuate or move inside a well-built building	Move to basement of a well-built building

SECTION 3 · Floods

Key Ideas

◆ Floods occur when so much water pours into a stream or river that it overflows its banks on either side of the channel.

◆ The first rule of flood safety: Move to higher ground and stay away from flood waters.

Key Term

flash flood

SECTION 4 · Predicting the Weather

Key Ideas

◆ Meteorologists interpret weather information from local weather observers, instruments carried by balloons, satellites, and weather stations around the world.

◆ Changes in weather technology have occurred in two areas: gathering weather data and using computers to make forecasts.

◆ Standard symbols on weather maps show fronts, areas of high and low pressure, types of precipitation, and temperatures.

Key Terms

meteorologist	isobar
El Niño	isotherm

SECTION 1 — What Causes Climate?

Key Ideas

◆ The climate of a region is determined by its temperature and precipitation.

◆ The main factors that influence temperature are latitude, altitude, distance from large bodies of water, and ocean currents.

◆ The main factors that affect precipitation are prevailing winds and the presence of mountains.

◆ The different seasons are a result of the tilt of Earth's axis as Earth travels around the sun.

Key Terms

climate   continental climate
tropical zone   windward
polar zone   leeward
temperate zone   microclimate
marine climate

FACTORS AFFECTING CLIMATE

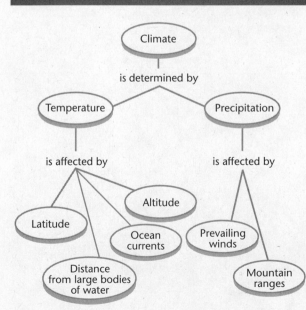

SECTION 2 — Climate Regions

Key Ideas

◆ Climates are classified according to temperature and precipitation.

◆ There are five main climate regions: tropical rainy, dry, temperate marine, temperate continental, and polar. Highlands are often considered to be a sixth climate region.

Key Terms

rain forest   steppe   subarctic
savanna   humid   tundra
desert   subtropical   permafrost

SECTION 3 — Long-Term Changes in Climate

Key Ideas

◆ During each ice age, huge sheets of ice covered much of Earth's surface.

◆ Possible explanations for major climate changes include movement of continents, variations in the position of Earth relative to the sun, and changes in the sun's energy output.

Key Terms

ice age   sunspot

SECTION 4 — Global Changes in the Atmosphere

Key Ideas

◆ Human activities that add greenhouse gases to the atmosphere may be warming Earth's atmosphere.

◆ Chemicals produced by humans have been damaging the ozone layer.

Key Terms

greenhouse gas   chlorofluorocarbons
global warming

EARTH SCIENCE

© Pearson Education, Inc.

EARTH SCIENCE

TOPIC 5

ASTRONOMY

SECTION 1　Earth in Space

Key Ideas

◆ Astronomy is the study of the moon, stars, and other objects in space.
◆ Earth's rotation on its axis causes day and night.
◆ One complete revolution of Earth around the sun is called a year.
◆ Earth has seasons because its axis is tilted as it revolves around the sun.

Key Terms

astronomy	latitude
axis	solstice
rotation	equinox
revolution	vernal equinox
orbit	autumnal equinox

HOW EARTH MOVES

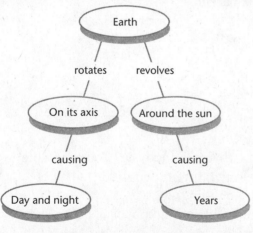

SECTION 2　Phases, Eclipses, and Tides

Key Ideas

◆ The moon revolves around Earth and rotates on its own axis.
◆ The phase of the moon you see depends on how much of the sunlit side faces Earth.
◆ A solar eclipse occurs when the moon passes between Earth and the sun, blocking the sunlight from reaching Earth.
◆ A lunar eclipse occurs when Earth is directly between the moon and the sun, blocking the sunlight from reaching the moon.
◆ Differences in how much the moon pulls on different parts of Earth cause tides.

Key Terms

phase	lunar eclipse
eclipse	tide
solar eclipse	gravity
umbra	spring tide
penumbra	neap tide

SECTION 3　Rockets and Satellites

Key Ideas

◆ A rocket moves in one direction when gases are expelled from it in the opposite direction.
◆ Satellites and space stations are used for communications, navigation, collecting weather data, and research.

Key Terms

satellite	geosynchronous orbit

SECTION 4　Earth's Moon

Key Ideas

◆ Features on the moon's surface include craters, highlands, and maria.
◆ Much of what scientists know about the moon came from studying moon rocks.

Key Terms

telescope	crater	maria

EARTH SCIENCE

SECTION 1 — Observing the Solar System

Key Ideas

◆ Ptolemy thought that Earth is at the center of the system of planets.

◆ Copernicus thought that the sun is at the center of the planets. Galileo's observations supported Copernicus's theory.

◆ Kepler discovered that the orbits of the planets are ellipses.

◆ Newton concluded that two factors—inertia and gravity—combine to keep the planets in orbit.

Key Terms

geocentric   ellipse
heliocentric   inertia

 **SECTION 2 — The Sun**

Key Ideas

◆ The sun's energy comes from nuclear fusion.

◆ The sun's atmosphere has three layers: photosphere, chromosphere, and corona.

◆ Features on or above the sun's surface include sunspots, prominences, and solar flares.

Key Terms

nuclear fusion   solar wind
core   sunspot
photosphere   prominence
chromosphere   solar flare
corona

 **SECTION 3 — The Inner Planets**

Key Idea

◆ The four inner planets (Mercury, Venus, Earth, and Mars) are small, with rocky surfaces. They are called the terrestrial planets.

Key Terms

terrestrial planets   greenhouse effect
retrograde rotation

 SECTION 4 — The Outer Planets

Key Ideas

◆ Four outer planets—Jupiter, Saturn, Uranus, and Neptune—are much larger than Earth.

◆ Pluto and Charon have solid surfaces and masses much less than that of Earth.

Key Term

gas giant

SECTION 5 — Comets, Asteroids, and Meteors

Key Ideas

◆ Comets are chunks of ice and dust that usually have long, elliptical orbits.

◆ Most asteroids revolve around the sun between the orbits of Mars and Jupiter.

Key Terms

comet   asteroid belt   meteor
asteroid   meteoroid   meteorite

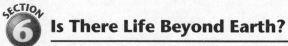 **SECTION 6 — Is There Life Beyond Earth?**

Key Ideas

◆ Earth has liquid water and a suitable temperature range and atmosphere for living things to survive.

◆ Since life as we know it requires water, scientists hypothesize that Mars may have once had the conditions for life to exist.

Key Term

extraterrestrial life

EARTH SCIENCE

SECTION 1 Tools of Modern Astronomy

Key Ideas

◆ The EMS includes radio waves, infrared radiation, visible light, ultraviolet radiation, X-rays, and gamma rays.

◆ Telescopes collect and focus different types of electromagnetic radiation.

◆ Astronomers use spectrographs to get information about stars.

Key Terms

constellation
visible light
electromagnetic
  radiation
wavelength
spectrum

refracting telescope
convex lens
reflecting telescope
radio telescope
observatory
spectrograph

TYPES OF TELESCOPES

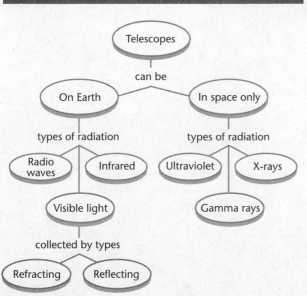

SECTION 2 Characteristics of Stars

Key Ideas

◆ Astronomers use parallax to measure distances to nearby stars.

◆ The main characteristics used to classify stars are size, temperature, and brightness.

Key Terms

galaxy
universe
light-year
parallax
giant star

apparent magnitude
absolute magnitude
Hertzsprung-Russell diagram
main sequence

SECTION 3 Lives of Stars

Key Ideas

◆ A star is born when nuclear fusion starts.

◆ A star's lifespan depends on its mass.

◆ When a star runs out of fuel, it becomes a white dwarf, a neutron star, or a black hole.

Key Terms

pulsar
nebula
protostar

white dwarf
supernova
neutron star

black hole
quasar

SECTION 4 Star Systems and Galaxies

Key Ideas

◆ More than half of all stars are members of groups of stars, called star systems.

◆ There are three types of galaxies: spiral, elliptical, and irregular.

Key Terms

binary star
eclipsing binary
spiral galaxy

elliptical galaxy
irregular galaxy

SECTION 5 History of the Universe

Key Ideas

◆ According to the big bang theory, the universe formed in an enormous explosion about 10 to 15 billion years ago.

◆ About five billion years ago, a cloud of gas and dust collapsed to form the solar system.

Key Term

big bang

EARTH SCIENCE

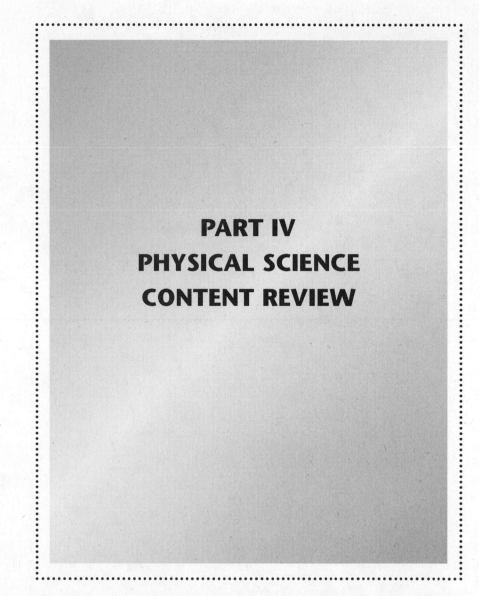

PART IV
PHYSICAL SCIENCE
CONTENT REVIEW

TOPIC 1

CHEMICAL BUILDING BLOCKS

SECTION 1 Describing Matter

Key Ideas

◆ Matter makes up everything in the universe. The three commonly found states of matter are solid, liquid, and gas.

◆ The characteristic properties of a substance can be used to identify the substance.

◆ Physical changes alter the form of a substance, but not its identity. In chemical changes, one or more substances combine or decompose to form new substances.

◆ Matter can be classified into two general categories: mixtures and pure substances. The pure substances include elements and compounds.

Key Terms

characteristic property	mixture
boiling point	solution
melting point	pure substance
physical change	element
chemical change	compound
chemical activity	

CLASSIFYING MATTER

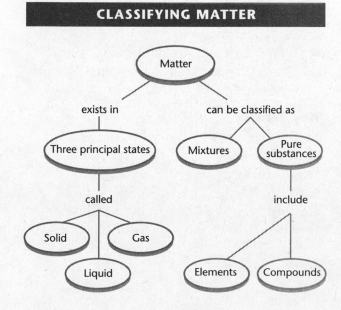

SECTION 2 Measuring Matter

Key Ideas

◆ Mass is a measurement of how much matter an object contains. If you move an object away from Earth, its weight changes but its mass stays the same.

◆ The density of an object equals its mass divided by its volume. A unit of density is always a mass unit divided by a volume unit, such as grams per cubic centimeter (g/cm^3).

Key Terms

weight	volume
mass	density
International System of Units (SI)	

SECTION 3 Particles of Matter

Key Ideas

◆ Atoms are the smallest particles of an element.

◆ Dalton stated that atoms are unbreakable, rigid spheres. He also said that atoms of different elements are different from one another.

◆ Atoms can be combined into molecules, which are held together by chemical bonds.

Key Terms

SECTION 4 Elements From Earth

Key Ideas

◆ Gold can be separated from other materials because of its density.

◆ Earth contains deposits of many elements in the form of compounds. A chemical reaction is needed to remove an element from its compound.

Key Terms

© Pearson Education, Inc.

PHYSICAL SCIENCE

PHYSICAL SCIENCE

SECTION 1 Solids, Liquids, and Gases

Key Ideas

◆ Solids have a definite shape and volume because the particles in a solid are packed tightly together and stay in fixed positions.

◆ The particles in a liquid are free to move around one another. Thus, a liquid has no definite shape, but it does have a definite volume.

◆ The particles of a gas spread apart to fill all the space available to them. Thus, a gas has neither definite shape nor definite volume.

Key Terms

solid	fluid
crystalline solid	viscosity
amorphous solid	gas
liquid	

STATES OF MATTER

State of Matter	Shape	Volume	Example (at room temperature)
Solid	Definite	Definite	Diamond
Liquid	Not definite	Definite	Water
Gas	Not definite	Not definite	Oxygen

SECTION 2 Behavior of Gases

Key Ideas

◆ At constant temperature, when the volume of a gas decreases, its pressure increases.

◆ In a rigid container, raising the temperature of a gas increases its pressure.

◆ In a flexible container, raising the temperature of a gas increases its volume.

Key Terms

temperature	Boyle's law
pressure	Charles's law

SECTION 3 Graphing Gas Behavior

Key Ideas

◆ A graph shows that the volume of a gas and its kelvin temperature are directly proportional at constant pressure.

◆ A graph shows that the pressure of a gas at constant temperature varies inversely with its volume.

Key Terms

graph	vary inversely
directly proportional	

SECTION 4 Physical and Chemical Changes

Key Ideas

◆ In a physical change, substances change form but not their identities. In a chemical change, substances change into other substances.

◆ Matter changes whenever energy is added to or taken away from it.

◆ Changes of state occur when a substance gains or loses energy and the particles of the substance are rearranged.

◆ Chemical changes are also called chemical reactions. Chemical reactions either absorb or release energy.

Key Terms

thermal energy	vaporization
chemical energy	evaporation
law of conservation of energy	boiling
	condensation
melting	sublimation
freezing	chemical reaction

SECTION 1   Organizing the Elements

Key Ideas

◆ Mendeleev developed the first periodic table of the elements. An element's properties can be predicted from its location in the periodic table.

◆ Each square of the periodic table may contain the atomic number, chemical symbol, name, and atomic mass of an element.

◆ The main body of the periodic table is arranged into 18 columns, called groups, and 7 rows, called periods.

◆ The properties of each element can be predicted from its location in the periodic table.

Key Terms

atomic mass	atomic number
periodic table	chemical symbol
nucleus	group
proton	family
neutron	period
electron	valence electron
atomic mass unit (amu)	

THE PERIODIC TABLE

SECTION 2   Metals

Key Ideas

◆ Most of the elements are metals. Metals are found to the left of the zigzag line in the periodic table.

◆ Metals are usually shiny, ductile, malleable, and good conductors of heat and electricity.

◆ The reactivity of metals tends to decrease as you move from left to right across the periodic table.

Key Terms

malleable	corrosion	transition
ductile	alloy	metal
conductor	alkaline metal	lanthanide
magnetic	alkaline	actinide
reactivity	earth metal	

SECTION 3   Nonmetals and Metalloids

Key Ideas

◆ Nonmetals, found to the right of the zigzag line, are often gases or dull, brittle solids with low melting points.

◆ Metalloids have characteristics of both metals and nonmetals.

Key Terms

nonmetal	noble gas
diatomic molecule	metalloid
halogen family	semiconductor

SECTION 4   Elements From Stardust

Key Ideas

◆ Nuclear fusion inside stars produces the nuclei of different light elements, such as helium.

◆ Elements heavier than iron are produced in a supernova, the explosion of a very massive star.

Key Terms

plasma	nuclear fusion	supernova

PHYSICAL SCIENCE

SECTION 1 — Chemical Bonds, Carbon Style

Key Ideas

◆ Carbon atoms can form bonds with one another and with atoms of other elements to form a large number of different compounds.

◆ The element carbon exists in different forms. Diamond crystals are the hardest mineral formed in Earth. Graphite is a slippery form of carbon. Fullerenes have an open, spherelike shape.

Key Terms

diamond   graphite   fullerene

SECTION 2 — Carbon Compounds

Key Ideas

◆ Many organic compounds have properties in common with one another.

◆ Carbon chains in hydrocarbons can be straight, branched, or ring-shaped.

◆ Isomers are different from one another because of their differing structural formula.

◆ Substituted hydrocarbons, which are related to other hydrocarbons, include halogen-containing compounds, alcohols, and organic acids.

◆ Polymers are formed from many monomers linked together.

Key Terms

organic compound	hydroxyl group
hydrocarbon	alcohol
molecular formula	organic acid
subscript	carboxyl group
structural formula	ester
isomer	polymer
saturated hydrocarbon	monomer
unsaturated hydrocarbon	synthetic
substituted hydrocarbon	

SECTION 3 — Life With Carbon

Key Ideas

◆ Nutrients provide your body with energy and raw materials. Many nutrients are organic compounds made of large molecules.

◆ The four main classes of organic compounds in living things are carbohydrates, proteins, lipids, and nucleic acids.

◆ Complex carbohydrates are built from sugars. The building blocks of proteins are amino acids. Fats and oils are made from fatty acids and glycerol. Nucleic acids are made from nucleotides.

◆ Vitamins and minerals are other nutrients that contribute to a healthy diet.

Key Terms

nutrient	lipid
digestion	fatty acid
carbohydrate	cholesterol
glucose	nucleic acid
complex carbohydrate	DNA
starch	RNA
cellulose	nucleotide
protein	vitamin
amino acid	mineral

PROTEINS AND NUCLEIC ACIDS

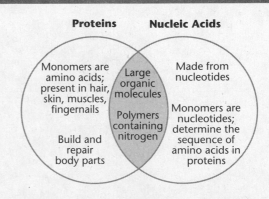

TOPIC 2

CHEMICAL INTERACTIONS

PHYSICAL SCIENCE

SECTION 1 — Matter and Changes in Matter

Key Ideas
◆ Matter may be in the form of elements, compounds, or mixtures.
◆ Chemical changes result in the formation of new substances. Physical changes do not.
◆ Chemical reactions occur when chemical bonds are formed or broken.

Key Terms
chemistry
element
compound
mixture
solution
physical change

chemical change
chemical reaction
precipitate
atom
molecule
chemical bond

SECTION 2 — Describing Chemical Reactions

Key Ideas
◆ A chemical equation uses symbols for the reactants and products of a chemical reaction.
◆ Chemical reactions may be classified by the types of changes in reactants and products.

Key Terms
chemical equation
symbol
chemical formula
subscript
reactants
products

conservation of mass
coefficient
synthesis
decomposition
replacement

SECTION 3 — Controlling Chemical Reactions

Key Ideas
◆ A chemical reaction involves a change in energy.
◆ Concentration, surface area, temperature, catalysts, and inhibitors affect the rate of chemical reactions.

Key Terms
exothermic reaction
endothermic reaction
activation energy
concentration

catalyst
enzyme
inhibitor

CHARACTERISTICS OF CHEMICAL REACTIONS

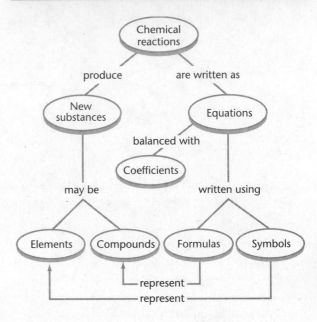

SECTION 4 — Fire and Fire Safety

Key Ideas
◆ The fire triangle shows the three things necessary to start a fire and keep it burning: fuel, oxygen, and heat.
◆ Water stops combustion by keeping the fuel from coming in contact with oxygen. Also, evaporation of water uses a great deal of heat and cools the fire.

Key Terms
combustion   fuel

SECTION 1 **Inside an Atom**

Key Ideas
◆ An atom consists of a nucleus of protons and neutrons, surrounded by rapidly moving electrons.
◆ Chemical reactions involve the valence electrons of atoms. Chemical bonds form when electrons are transferred or shared between atoms.

Key Terms
nucleus   electron
proton   valence electron
neutron   electron dot diagram

SECTION 2 **Atoms in the Periodic Table**

Key Ideas
◆ The periodic table organizes the elements according to atomic number.
◆ Families of elements have similar properties.
◆ The noble gases (Group 18) are the least reactive elements. Elements in groups 1 and 17 are highly reactive.

Key Terms
atomic number   period
group   halogen
family

SECTION 3 **Ionic Bonds**

Key Ideas
◆ Ions form when atoms become charged after gaining or losing electrons.
◆ Ionic compounds exist as crystals made of many ions, each attracted to all the surrounding ions of opposite charge.
◆ Ionic compounds have high melting and boiling points. They conduct electricity when dissolved in water.

Key Terms
ion   polyatomic ion
ionic bond   crystal

 SECTION 4 **Covalent Bonds**

Key Ideas
◆ In covalent bonds, pairs of electrons are shared between atoms.
◆ In polar covalent bonds, the shared electrons are attracted more to one atom than the other.
◆ Attractions between polar molecules are stronger than attractions between nonpolar molecules, leading to differences in properties.

Key Terms
covalent bond   molecular   polar
double bond   compound   nonpolar

COMPARING IONIC AND MOLECULAR COMPOUNDS

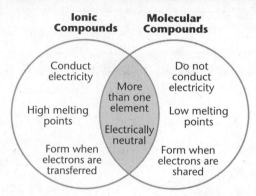

SECTION 5 **Crystal Chemistry**

Key Ideas
◆ Minerals have characteristic properties, such as hardness, density, color, crystal shape, and the way the crystal breaks and grows.
◆ The properties of a mineral depend on its chemical composition and its bonding.
◆ The stronger the chemical bonds in a mineral crystal, the harder the crystal is.

Key Term
mineral

PHYSICAL SCIENCE

Skills and Content Review

PHYSICAL SCIENCE

SECTION 1   Working With Solutions

Key Ideas

◆ A solution is a well-mixed mixture. Particles dissolved in a liquid solution cannot be seen or separated by settling or filtration.

◆ In a solution, solute particles separate from each other and become surrounded by particles of the solvent.

◆ Every solute has a specific solubility in a particular solvent. Solubility changes with temperature, pressure, and type of solvent.

◆ Solutes affect the freezing points and boiling points of solvents.

Key Terms

suspension   concentrated solution
solution   solubility
solvent   saturated solution
solute   unsaturated solution
dilute solution

CHARACTERISTICS OF SOLUTIONS

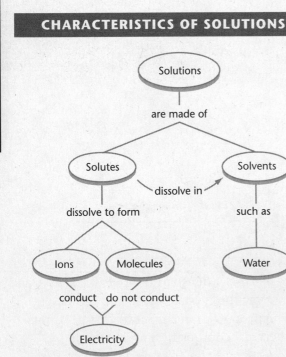

SECTION 2   Describing Acids and Bases

Key Ideas

◆ An acid tastes sour, reacts with metals and carbonates, and turns blue litmus paper red.

◆ A base tastes bitter, feels slippery, and turns red litmus paper blue.

◆ An indicator is a substance that turns different colors in an acid or a base.

Key Terms

acid   indicator
corrosive   base

SECTION 3   Acids and Bases in Solution

Key Ideas

◆ An acid produces hydrogen ions (H^+) when it dissolves in water. A base produces hydroxide ions (OH^-) when it dissolves in water.

◆ pH describes the acidity of a solution.

Key Terms

hydrogen ion (H^+)   acid rain
hydroxide ion (OH^-)   neutralization
pH scale   salt

SECTION 4   Digestion and pH

Key Ideas

◆ Digestion breaks foods into smaller molecules.

◆ Each digestive enzyme works best at a specific pH.

Key Terms

digestion   chemical digestion
mechanical digestion

Polymers and Composites

Key Ideas

◆ Polymers are large compounds made of many small molecules called monomers.

◆ Polymers occur as products of living cells. Polymers also are synthesized in factories and laboratories for a variety of uses.

◆ Composite materials combine the useful properties of two different substances.

Key Terms

polymer   cellulose   composite
monomer   plastic

Metals and Alloys

Key Ideas

◆ An alloy is a mixture of two or more elements, one of which is a metal. Alloys have the properties of metals, as well as other useful properties.

◆ Steel is one of the most frequently used alloys. Its strength and resistance to corrosion make it useful in such things as building materials, tools, and machinery.

Key Term

alloy

Ceramics and Glass

Key Ideas

◆ Ceramics are made by heating clay mixed with other materials to temperatures that produce a brittle, crystalline solid. Food storage, building materials, and heat insulators are some uses of ceramics.

◆ Glass results when sand is melted to make a thick liquid that can be shaped when hot. Adding other materials gives glass properties such as heat resistance and color.

Key Terms

ceramics   glass   optical fiber

PROPERTIES OF MATERIALS

Material	Made From	How Made	How Used
Polymers	Monomers (carbon compounds)	Chemical bonds link monomers in a repeating pattern	Fabrics, packaging materials, household items, toys, containers, insulation
Alloys	Metals and other elements	Metals heated and mixed	Construction materials, jewelry, tools, machinery, hardware
Ceramics	Clay; other materials	Heated until crystalline solid forms	Containers, insulating materials, building materials
Glass	Sand	Melted, then cooled in desired shapes	Windows, lenses, glassware, cookware, optical fibers

Radioactive Elements

Key Ideas

◆ Radioactive decay is a change in the nucleus of an atom that releases particles and energy. The products of such decay are alpha and beta particles and gamma rays.

◆ Half-life is the time it takes for half of the radioactive atoms of an isotope to decay.

◆ Radioactive isotopes are used as sources of radiation in industry and medicine.

Key Terms

nuclear reaction   beta particle
isotope   gamma radiation
mass number   half-life
radioactive decay   radioactive dating
nuclear radiation   tracer
alpha particle   radiation therapy

PHYSICAL SCIENCE

© Pearson Education, Inc.

TOPIC 3

MOTION, FORCES, AND ENERGY

Chapter 1: Motion
Chapter 2: Forces
Chapter 3: Forces in Fluids
Chapter 4: Work and Machines
Chapter 5: Energy and Power
Chapter 6: Thermal Energy and Heat

Describing and Measuring Motion

Key Ideas

◆ The motion of an object is determined by its change of position relative to a reference point.

◆ Speed is the distance an object travels per one unit of time. If an object moves at constant speed, its speed can be determined by dividing the distance it travels by the time taken. If an object's speed varies, then dividing distance by time gives you the object's average speed.

◆ When you state both the speed of an object and the direction in which it is moving, you are describing the object's velocity.

◆ The slope of a distance-time graph represents speed. The steeper the slope, the faster the speed.

Key Terms

motion	meter
reference point	speed
International System of Units (SI)	velocity

Slow Motion on Planet Earth

Key Idea

◆ The plates that make up Earth's outer layer move very slowly, only centimeters per year, in various directions.

Key Term

plate

 Acceleration

Key Ideas

◆ Acceleration is the rate at which velocity changes. It involves increasing speed, decreasing speed, or changing direction.

◆ Acceleration can be calculated by dividing the change in velocity by the amount of time it took that change to occur.

Key Term

acceleration

DESCRIBING AND MEASURING MOTION

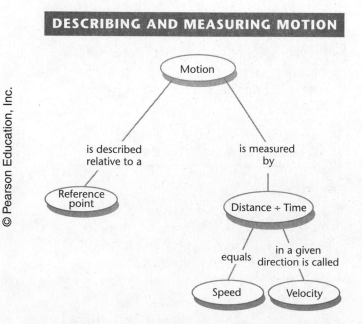

PHYSICAL SCIENCE

The Nature of Force

Key Ideas
◆ The sum of all the forces acting on an object is the net force.
◆ Unbalanced forces change the motion of an object, whereas balanced forces do not.
◆ According to Newton's first law of motion, an object at rest will remain at rest and an object in motion will continue in motion at constant speed unless the object is acted upon by an unbalanced force.

Key Terms
force

net force

unbalanced forces

balanced forces

inertia

mass

Force, Mass, and Acceleration

Key Idea
◆ Newton's second law of motion states that the net force on an object is the product of its acceleration and its mass.

Key Term
newton

Friction and Gravity

Key Ideas
◆ Friction is a force that one surface exerts on another when they rub against each other.
◆ Weight is a measure of the force of gravity on an object, and mass is a measure of the amount of matter that an object contains.
◆ The force of gravity acts between all objects in the universe.

Key Terms
friction

sliding friction

rolling friction

fluid friction

gravity

free fall

projectile

air resistance

terminal velocity

weight

FRICTION AND GRAVITY

Force	Direction of Force	Force Depends Upon
Friction	opposite to the direction of the motion	types of surfaces and how hard the surfaces push together
Gravity	between any two objects	masses and distances

 Action and Reaction

Key Ideas
◆ Newton's third law of motion states that every time there is an action force on an object, the object will exert an equal and opposite reaction force.
◆ The momentum of an object is the product of its mass and its velocity.
◆ The law of conservation of momentum states that the total momentum is the same before and after an event, as long as there are no outside forces.

Key Terms
momentum

law of conservation of momentum

Orbiting Satellites

Key Ideas
◆ A rocket burns fuel and produces gases. The rocket pushes these gases downward. At the same time, the gases apply an equal force to the rocket, pushing it upward.
◆ Even though a satellite is pulled downward by gravity, it stays in orbit because it is moving so quickly. Earth's surface curves away from the satellite as the satellite falls.

Key Terms
satellite   centripetal force

© Pearson Education, Inc.

SECTION 1 — Pressure

Key Ideas

◆ Pressure is the force per unit area on a surface.

◆ Fluid pressure results from the motion of the atoms or molecules that make up the fluid.

◆ Pressure at a given level in a fluid is the same in all directions. Pressure decreases with altitude and increases with depth.

Key Terms

pressure   fluid
pascal

HOW A HYDRAULIC DEVICE MULTIPLIES FORCE

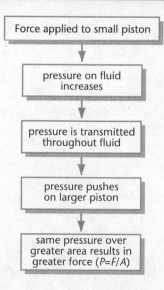

Force applied to small piston

↓

pressure on fluid increases

↓

pressure is transmitted throughout fluid

↓

pressure pushes on larger piston

↓

same pressure over greater area results in greater force ($P=F/A$)

 SECTION 2 — Transmitting Pressure in a Fluid

Key Ideas

◆ According to Pascal's principle, an increase in pressure on a confined fluid is transmitted equally to all parts of the fluid.

◆ A hydraulic device works by transmitting an increase in pressure from one part of a confined fluid to the other. A small force exerted over a small area at one place results in a large force exerted by a larger area at another place.

Key Terms

Pascal's principle   hydraulic system

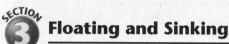 **SECTION 3 — Floating and Sinking**

Key Ideas

◆ The upward force on an object submerged in a fluid is called the buoyant force.

◆ The buoyant force on an object is equal to the weight of the fluid displaced by the object. This is Archimedes' principle.

◆ An object will sink, rise to the surface, or stay where it is in a fluid depending on whether its density is less than, greater than, or equal to the density of the fluid.

Key Terms

buoyant force   density
Archimedes' principle

 **SECTION 4 — Applying Bernoulli's Principle**

Key Idea

◆ The pressure in a fluid decreases as the speed of the fluid increases. This is Bernoulli's principle.

Key Term

Bernoulli's principle

PHYSICAL SCIENCE

SECTION 1   What Is Work?

Key Ideas

◆ Work is done on an object when a force causes that object to move some distance.

◆ The amount of work done on an object is equal to the force on the object in the direction of its motion multiplied by the distance the object moves.

$$Work = Force \times Distance$$

Key Terms

work   joule

SECTION 2   Mechanical Advantage and Efficiency

Key Ideas

◆ A machine makes work easier by changing the direction or amount of force needed to accomplish a task.

◆ The efficiency of a machine is the percentage of the input work that is changed to output work.

$$Efficiency = \frac{Output\ work}{Input\ work} \times 100\%$$

◆ The mechanical advantage of a machine is obtained by dividing the output force by the input force.

$$Mechanical\ advantage = \frac{Output\ force}{Input\ force}$$

◆ The ideal mechanical advantage of a machine is the mechanical advantage that it would have if there were no friction.

Key Terms

machine   efficiency
input force   actual mechanical
output force   advantage
mechanical   ideal mechanical
    advantage   advantage

PHYSICAL SCIENCE

SECTION 3   Simple Machines

Key Ideas

◆ There are six kinds of simple machines.

◆ A compound machine is a machine that is made from two or more simple machines.

Key Terms

inclined plane   wheel and axle
wedge   pulley
screw   compound machine
lever   gears
fulcrum

HOW TO CALCULATE THE MECHANICAL ADVANTAGE OF SIMPLE MACHINES

Simple Machine	Mechanical Advantage	Example
Inclined plane	Length of incline ÷ height of incline	Ramp
Lever	Distance from fulcrum to input force ÷ distance from fulcrum to output force	Seesaw, crowbar, fishing pole, wheelbarrow
Wheel and Axle	Distance from center of wheel to outside of wheel ÷ distance from center of axle to outside of axle	Hand mixer, screwdriver, doorknob, steering wheel
Pulley	Number of sections of rope supporting the load	Block and tackle, flag-pole lifting

SECTION 4   Machines in the Human Body

Key Ideas

◆ Most of the machines in your body are levers that consist of bones with muscles attached.

◆ When you bite into something, your front teeth function as a wedge.

Key Term

tendon

SECTION 1 The Nature of Energy

Key Ideas

- Energy is the ability to do work or produce change.
- Energy is transferred from one object to another when work is done.
- Kinetic energy is the energy that an object has because of its motion. Potential energy is the energy an object has because of its position or condition.
- Six forms of energy are mechanical energy, thermal energy, chemical energy, electric energy, electromagnetic energy, and nuclear energy.

Key Terms

energy
kinetic energy
potential energy
elastic potential energy
gravitational potential energy

mechanical energy
thermal energy
chemical energy
electrical energy
electromagnetic energy
nuclear energy

SECTION 2 Energy Conversion and Conservation

Key Ideas

- An energy conversion or transformation occurs when energy changes from one form to another.
- In any process, no energy is lost. This is the law of conservation of energy.

Key Terms

energy conversion

law of conservation of energy

SECTION 3 Energy Conversions and Fossil Fuels

Key Ideas

- Energy from the sun is converted to chemical energy in plants and animals. Fossil fuels, such as coal and petroleum, were formed from the remains of ancient plants and animals.
- The energy in fossil fuels is released and transformed when the fuels are burned.

Key Term

fossil fuels

SECTION 4 Power

Key Ideas

- Power is the rate at which work is done, or the rate at which energy is transformed.
- Power is calculated by dividing the amount of work done (or energy converted) by the time it took. The unit of power is the watt: 1 W = 1 J/s.

Key Term

power

PHYSICAL SCIENCE

ENERGY, WORK, AND POWER

Energy

exists as — Kinetic energy, Potential energy

measured in — Joules

is the ability to do — Work

Potential energy can be — Elastic, Gravitational

Work which at a given rate is — Power

SECTION 1 — Temperature and Thermal Energy

Key Ideas
◆ Temperature is a measure of the average kinetic energy of each particle within an object.
◆ Three temperature scales are Fahrenheit, Celsius, and Kelvin.
◆ Thermal energy is the total energy of the particles that make up an object.

Key Terms
temperature
Fahrenheit scale
Celsius scale
Kelvin scale
absolute zero

HEAT

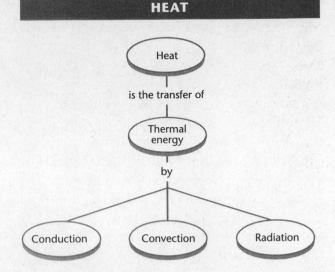

SECTION 2 — The Nature of Heat

Key Ideas
◆ Heat is a transfer of thermal energy from an object at a higher temperature to an object at a lower temperature.
◆ Heat is transferred by conduction, convection, and radiation.
◆ A conductor transfers heat well, whereas an insulator does not.
◆ The amount of heat necessary to raise a unit of mass of a substance by a specific unit of temperature is called the specific heat.

Key Terms
heat
conduction
convection
convection current
radiation
conductor
insulator
specific heat

SECTION 3 — Thermal Energy and States of Matter

Key Idea
◆ Matter can undergo a change of state when thermal energy is added or removed.

Key Terms
state
change of state
melting
melting point
freezing
freezing point
vaporization
evaporation
boiling
boiling point
condensation
thermal expansion
thermostat
bimetallic strip

SECTION 4 — Uses of Heat

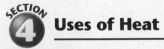

Key Ideas
◆ A heat engine converts thermal energy to mechanical energy that can do work.
◆ A refrigerator transfers thermal energy from a cool region to a warm region.

Key Terms
heat engine
combustion
external combustion engine
internal combustion engine

TOPIC 4

ELECTRICITY AND MAGNETISM

PHYSICAL SCIENCE

© Pearson Education, Inc.

Chapter 1 Magnetism and Electromagnetism

SECTION 1 The Nature of Magnetism

Key Ideas

◆ Unlike magnetic poles attract; like magnetic poles repel.

◆ A magnetic field is a region around a magnet in which magnetic attraction acts.

◆ Magnetic domains are regions in which the magnetic fields of atoms are aligned.

◆ In a magnetized material, most of the domains are lined up in the same direction.

Key Terms

magnetism   nucleus
magnetic pole   proton
magnetic field   electron
magnetic field lines   magnetic domain
atom   ferromagnetic material
element   permanent magnet

MAGNETISM

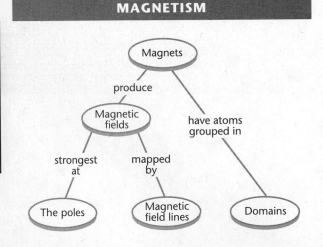

SECTION 2 Magnetic Earth

Key Ideas

◆ Earth has a north and a south magnetic pole.

◆ A compass needle lines up with Earth's magnetic poles.

◆ Earth's magnetic poles are not at exactly the same locations as the geographic poles.

◆ The magnetosphere is the magnetic field of Earth as shaped by the solar wind.

Key Terms

compass   solar wind
magnetic declination   magnetosphere
Van Allen belts   aurora

SECTION 3 Electric Currents and Magnetic Fields

Key Ideas

◆ Electric current is electric charge in motion.

◆ An electric current produces a magnetic field.

◆ Electric charges flow freely through materials called conductors but not through insulators.

◆ Resistance is the opposition to the movement of charges flowing through a material.

Key Terms

electric charge   insulator
electric current   resistor
electric circuit   resistance
conductor   superconductor

SECTION 4 Electromagnets

Key Ideas

◆ A solenoid creates a magnetic field by means of a current flowing through a coil of wire.

◆ The strength of an electromagnet depends on the amount of current, the number of turns of wire in the coil, how close together the turns of wire are, and the type of magnetic core.

Key Terms

solenoid   electromagnet

SECTION 1 — Electric Charge and Static Electricity

Key Ideas

◆ Like charges repel each other and unlike charges attract each other.

◆ An electric field is produced in the region around an electric charge. The field can be represented by electric field lines.

◆ Static electricity results when electrons move from one object to another, or from one location to another within an object.

◆ During an electric discharge, charges leave a charged object, making the object neutral.

Key Terms

electric field   induction
static electricity   conservation of charge
friction   static discharge
conduction   electroscope

SECTION 2 — Circuit Measurements

Key Ideas

◆ Electric current flows when voltage is applied to a circuit.

◆ Voltage, which is measured in volts, is the potential difference between two places in a circuit.

◆ Resistance, which is measured in ohms, is the opposition to the flow of charge.

◆ If resistance is held constant, an increase in voltage produces an increase in current.

◆ If voltage is held constant, an increase in resistance produces a decrease in current.

Key Terms

electrical potential   voltmeter
potential difference   ammeter
voltage   Ohm's law
voltage source

SECTION 3 — Series and Parallel Circuits

Key Ideas

◆ A series circuit is a circuit in which charges have only one path to flow through.

◆ A parallel circuit is a circuit that contains different branches through which charges can flow. Household circuits are parallel circuits.

Key Terms

series circuit   parallel circuit

TWO TYPES OF CIRCUITS

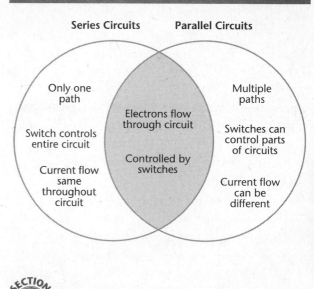

Series Circuits — Parallel Circuits

- Only one path
- Switch controls entire circuit
- Current flow same throughout circuit

- Electrons flow through circuit
- Controlled by switches

- Multiple paths
- Switches can control parts of circuits
- Current flow can be different

SECTION 4 — Electrical Safety

Key Ideas

◆ Fuses, circuit breakers, and grounded plugs are all important safety devices found in electric circuits.

◆ A lightning rod provides a conducting path to Earth, so that electric charges from lightning can travel directly into Earth without damaging a structure.

◆ The human body can be seriously injured by shocks, even those of less than one ampere.

Key Terms

short circuit   grounded   fuse
third prong   lightning rod   circuit breaker

PHYSICAL SCIENCE

© Pearson Education, Inc.

SECTION 1 — Electricity, Magnetism, and Motion

Key Ideas

◆ A magnetic field exerts a force on a wire carrying current, causing the wire to move.

◆ A galvanometer uses the magnetic force on a current-carrying wire to turn a pointer on a scale. The scale can then be used to measure current.

◆ An electric motor converts electrical energy into mechanical energy.

Key Terms

energy	electric motor
electrical energy	commutator
mechanical energy	brushes
galvanometer	armature

SECTION 2 — Generating Electric Current

Key Ideas

◆ A current is induced in a wire in a moving or changing magnetic field.

◆ Current that moves in one direction only is called direct current. Current that reverses direction is called alternating current.

◆ A generator converts mechanical energy into electrical energy.

◆ Mechanical energy is required to move a turbine. That energy can be supplied by falling water, the burning of fossil fuels, the wind, the sun, the tides, or steam from within Earth.

Key Terms

electromagnetic induction	slip rings
alternating current	turbine
direct current	renewable resource
electric generator	nonrenewable resource

GENERATING ELECTRIC CURRENT

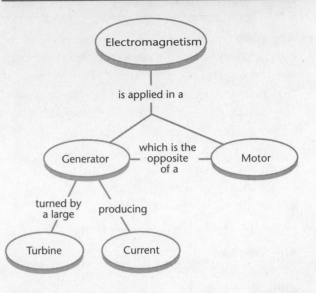

SECTION 3 — Using Electric Power

Key Ideas

◆ Power is the rate at which energy is converted.

◆ Transformers increase or decrease voltage.

◆ The voltage of alternating current can be stepped up and stepped down.

Key Terms

power	step-up transformer
transformer	step-down transformer

SECTION 4 — Batteries

Key Ideas

◆ An electrochemical cell consists of two different metals, called electrodes, and a substance through which charges can flow, called an electrolyte.

◆ In a battery, electrochemical cells are connected in series to increase the voltage.

Key Terms

chemical energy	electrode	wet cell
chemical reaction	electrolyte	dry cell
electrochemical cell	terminal	rechargeable battery
	battery	

PHYSICAL SCIENCE

SECTION 1 — Electronic Signals and Semiconductors

Key Idea
◆ Semiconductors are used to make solid-state devices such as integrated circuits.

Key Terms
electronics

electronic signal

analog signal

digital signal

semiconductor

solid-state component

diode

transistor

integrated circuit

vacuum tube

SECTION 2 — Electronic Communication

Key Ideas
◆ Sound is converted into electronic signals in radio and telephone transmitters.
◆ Electronic signals can be carried over long distances by electromagnetic waves.

Key Terms
electromagnetic wave

amplitude

frequency

amplitude modulation (AM)

frequency modulation (FM)

cathode-ray tube (CRT)

SECTION 3 — Computers

Key Idea
◆ Computer hardware includes the central processing unit, input devices, output devices, and memory storage devices.

Key Terms
binary system

bit

byte

computer hardware

central processing unit

input device

output device

random-access memory (RAM)

read-only memory (ROM)

disk drive

hard disk

diskette

optical disc

computer software

computer programmer

SECTION 4 — The Information Superhighway

Key Ideas
◆ Computers are connected by computer networks. The Internet is a network of host computers that extends around the world.
◆ Safe use of computer networks includes checking for viruses and using chat rooms with caution.

Key Terms
computer network

local area network (LAN)

wide area network (WAN)

Internet

World Wide Web

encryption

computer virus

chat room

intellectual property

freeware

shareware

TELEPHONE COMMUNICATION

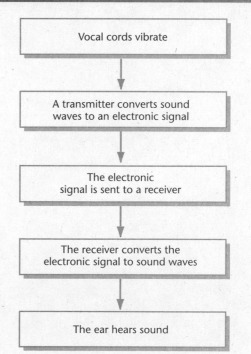

Vocal cords vibrate

↓

A transmitter converts sound waves to an electronic signal

↓

The electronic signal is sent to a receiver

↓

The receiver converts the electronic signal to sound waves

↓

The ear hears sound

PHYSICAL SCIENCE

TOPIC 5

SOUND AND LIGHT

What Are Waves?

Key Ideas

◆ Waves are created when a source of energy causes a medium to vibrate.

◆ The three types of waves are transverse waves, longitudinal waves, and surface waves.

Key Terms

wave	vibration	longitudinal
energy	transverse	wave
medium	wave	compression
mechanical	crest	rarefaction
wave	trough	surface wave

SECTION 2 Properties of Waves

Key Ideas

◆ The basic properties of waves are amplitude, wavelength, frequency, and speed.

◆ The speed, frequency, and wavelength of a wave are related by a mathematical formula.

Speed = Wavelength × Frequency

Key Terms

amplitude	frequency
wavelength	hertz (Hz)

SECTION 3 Interactions of Waves

Key Ideas

◆ When an object or wave hits a surface through which it cannot pass, it bounces back.

◆ When a wave moves from one medium into another medium at an angle, it changes speed as it enters the second medium and bends.

◆ When a wave passes a barrier or moves through a hole in a barrier, it bends and spreads out.

Key Terms

reflection	constructive interference
angle of incidence	destructive interference
angle of reflection	standing wave
refraction	node
diffraction	antinode
interference	resonance

 Seismic Waves

Key Ideas

◆ When stress in the rock beneath Earth's surface builds up enough, the rock breaks or changes shape, releasing energy in the form of seismic waves.

◆ Seismic waves include primary waves, secondary waves, and surface waves.

◆ A seismograph records the ground movements caused by seismic waves as they move through Earth.

Key Terms

seismic wave	tsunami
primary wave	seismograph
secondary wave	

PHYSICAL SCIENCE

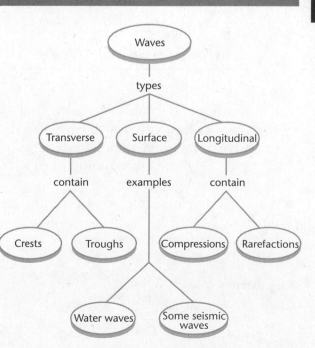

WAVES

© Pearson Education, Inc.

SECTION 1 — The Nature of Sound

Key Ideas

◆ Sound is a disturbance that travels through a medium as a longitudinal wave.

◆ The speed of sound depends on elasticity, density, and temperature of the medium.

Key Terms

larynx   elasticity   density

SECTION 2 — Properties of Sound

Key Ideas

◆ A sound wave of greater intensity sounds louder. Loudness is measured in decibels.

◆ The pitch of a sound that you hear depends on the frequency of the sound wave.

◆ As a sound source moves toward the listener, the waves reach the listener with a higher frequency. The pitch appears to increase because of the Doppler effect.

Key Terms

intensity   infrasound
loudness   pitch
decibels (dB)   Doppler effect
ultrasound

SECTION 3 — Combining Sound Waves

Key Ideas

◆ The blending of the fundamental tone and the overtones makes up the characteristic sound quality, or timbre, of a particular sound.

◆ Music is a set of tones that combine in ways that are pleasing to the ear.

◆ Noise has no pleasing timbre or identifiable pitch.

◆ Interference occurs when two or more sound waves interact.

Key Terms

timbre   noise   acoustics
music   dissonance   beats

SECTION 4 — How You Hear Sound

Key Idea

◆ The outer ear funnels sound waves, the middle ear transmits the sound waves inward, and the inner ear converts the sound waves into a form your brain can understand.

Key Terms

ear canal   eardrum   middle ear   cochlea

SECTION 5 — Applications of Sound

Key Ideas

◆ A sonar device measures the time it takes to detect reflected sound waves.

◆ Animals use sound waves to communicate, to navigate, and to find food.

Key Terms

sonar   echolocation   sonogram

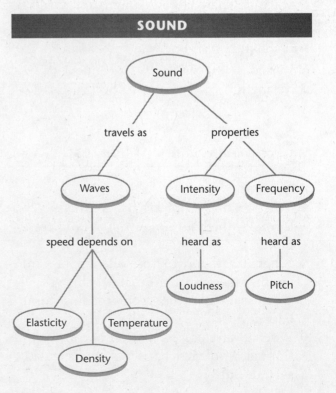

SECTION 1 — The Nature of Electromagnetic Waves

Key Ideas

◆ An electromagnetic wave transfers energy by means of changing electric and magnetic fields.

◆ Sometimes light acts as though it is a set of waves. Sometimes light acts as though it is a stream of particles.

Key Terms

electromagnetic wave

electromagnetic radiation

polarized light

photoelectric effect

photon

SECTION 2 — Waves of the Electromagnetic Spectrum

Key Ideas

◆ All electromagnetic waves travel at the same speed, but they have different wavelengths and different frequencies.

◆ Radio waves and the Doppler effect can be used to tell the speeds of moving objects.

Key Terms

electromagnetic spectrum

radio wave

microwave

radar

magnetic resonance imaging

infrared ray

thermogram

visible light

ultraviolet ray

X-ray

gamma ray

PROPERTIES OF ELECTROMAGNETIC WAVES

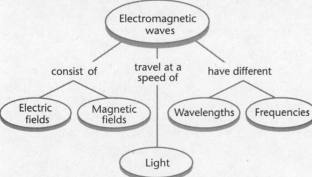

SECTION 3 — Producing Visible Light

Key Idea

◆ Light bulbs can be incandescent, fluorescent, neon, sodium vapor, or tungsten-halogen.

Key Terms

illuminated

luminous

spectroscope

incandescent light

fluorescent light

neon light

sodium vapor light

tungsten-halogen light

bioluminescence

SECTION 4 — Wireless Communication

Key Ideas

◆ At broadcasting stations, music and speech are converted from sound into an electrical signal and then into a pattern of changes in a radio wave.

◆ AM broadcasts transmit information by modifying the amplitude of the signal. FM broadcasts change the frequency of the signal.

◆ Cellular telephones transmit and receive signals using high-frequency radio waves.

◆ When you leave a message for a pager, the information is first sent to a receiving station. There it is coded and directed to the correct pager.

◆ Radio, television, and telephone signals are sent from Earth up to communications satellites, which then relay the signals to receivers around the world.

Key Terms

amplitude modulation (AM)

frequency modulation (FM)

PHYSICAL SCIENCE

Reflection and Mirrors

Key Ideas

◆ Light that strikes an object can be reflected, absorbed, or transmitted.

◆ A plane mirror produces an image that is right-side up and the same size as the object.

◆ Concave mirrors can form either virtual images or real images. Images formed by convex mirrors are always virtual.

Key Terms

opaque	plane mirror
transparent	virtual image
translucent	concave mirror
ray	focal point
regular reflection	real image
diffuse reflection	convex mirror
image	

MIRRORS

Type of Mirror	How It Affects Light	Type of Image Formed
Plane	Reflects	Virtual
Concave	Reflects	Real or virtual
Convex	Reflects	Virtual

 Refraction and Lenses

Key Ideas

◆ When light rays hit the surface of a medium at an angle, they bend, or change direction.

◆ The type of image formed by a convex lens depends on the position of the object in relation to the focal point.

◆ Concave lenses produce only virtual images.

Key Terms

index of refraction	concave lens
mirage	convex lens
lens	

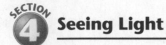 **Color**

Key Ideas

◆ You see an object as the color of the light it reflects. The primary colors of light are red, green, and blue.

◆ As pigments are added together, fewer colors of light are reflected and more are absorbed.

Key Terms

primary color	complementary color
secondary color	pigment

 Seeing Light

Key Ideas

◆ You see objects because of a series of steps that involve the structures of the eye and the brain.

◆ Lenses can correct some vision problems.

Key Terms

cornea	retina	optic nerve
iris	rod	nearsighted
pupil	cone	farsighted

 Using Light

Key Ideas

◆ A telescope uses lenses or mirrors to gather light.

◆ A laser beam consists of waves that all have the same wavelength. The waves are coherent.

Key Terms

telescope	camera
refracting telescope	laser
objective lens	hologram
eyepiece	optical fiber
reflecting telescope	total internal reflection
microscope	

PHYSICAL SCIENCE

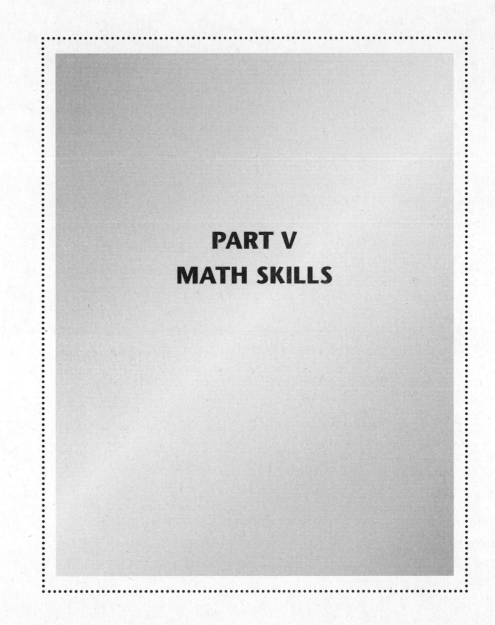

PART V
MATH SKILLS

Variables and Expressions

A **variable** is a quantity that can change or vary. Mathematicians use letters to represent variables.

A quantity that does not change is a **constant.**

An **expression** is a mathematical phrase involving constants, variables, and operation symbols. There are different ways to represent different operations. Four examples are shown below.

Addition:	$x + 6$	x is the variable.	6 is the constant.
Subtraction:	$91 - x$	x is the variable.	91 is the constant.
Multiplication:	$3x$ or $3 \times x$	x is the variable.	3 is the constant.
Division:	$12 \div x$ or $\frac{12}{x}$	x is the variable.	12 is the constant.

If you know the values of the variable, you can *evaluate* the expression by replacing the variable with each value. This is known as *substituting a value for the variable.*

 Example

Evaluate $2x$ for $x = 4, 6,$ and 8.

$2x$ means "2 times x." To evaluate the expression, you need to substitute a value for x.

When $x = 4$, substitute 4 for x: You can make a table to evaluate the expression for multiple values of x.

x	$2x$
4	$2 \times 4 = 8$
6	$2 \times 6 = 12$
8	$2 \times 8 = 16$

So $2x = 8$ when $x = 4$, $2x = 12$ when $x = 6$, and $2x = 16$ when $x = 8$.

MATH SKILLS

Skills and Content Review

Writing Expressions

Some words in English can be translated into specific mathematical operations (even if they have different meanings for everyday usage).

Word	Definition	Numerical Expression	Variable Expression
sum	The result of **adding** numbers	$7 + 2$	$8 + x$
difference	The result of **subtracting** numbers	$12 - 3$	$28 - y$
product	The result of **multiplying** numbers	4×16	$8c$
quotient	The result of **dividing** numbers	$81 \div 9$	$\frac{14}{s}$ or $14 \div s$

To translate situations that don't use these words, you need to choose an operation that is appropriate for the situation. It may be easier to choose an operation if you first replace the variable with a number.

 **Example**

Write an expression to answer: What is the quotient of 99 divided by x?

Step 1: What operation is being done? A quotient is the answer when dividing, so use division to write the expression.

Step 2: Use the appropriate sign to write the expression: $99 \div x$ or $\frac{99}{x}$

The expressions $99 \div x$ and $\frac{99}{x}$ shows the quotient of 99 divided by x.

MATH SKILLS

Using Equations

An **equation** is a mathematical sentence that uses an equal sign, =, to show that two expressions are equal. An equation can be either true or false. For example, $13 + 12 = 25$ is true because both sides of the equation (both sides of the equal sign) have the same value; $85 - 21 = 82$ is false because both sides of the equation do **not** have the same value.

An equation with a variable can also be true or false, depending on the value of the variable.

 Example

Is the equation true for the given value of the variable?

a. $4y = 24$, $y = 6$

$$4 \times 6 \overset{?}{=} 24 \qquad \text{Substitute 6 for } y.$$
$$24 = 24 \qquad \text{Multiply.}$$

Since both sides of the equation have the same value, the equation is true.

b. $8 + a = 10$, $a = 3$

$$8 + a \overset{?}{=} 10 \qquad \text{Substitute 3 for } a.$$
$$11 \neq 10 \qquad \text{Add.}$$

Since both sides of the equation do **not** have the same value, the equation is false.

Solving Equations

Sometimes you need to find the exact value that will make an equation true. This is known as *solving the equation.*

Think of equations as questions where the variable is read as "what number?" For example, $a + 3 = 10$ can be read as "What number plus 3 equals 10?" Use mental math to answer the question.

Example

Solve $y - 8 = 7$.

Step 1: Read as: "What number minus 8 equals 7?" $\qquad y - 8 = 7$

Step 2: Use mental math. $\qquad\qquad\qquad\qquad\qquad \mathbf{15} - 8 = 7$

Step 3: Check to see that the equation is true. $\qquad\quad 7 = 7 \checkmark$

In the equation $y - 8 = 7$, y is equal to 15.

MATH SKILLS

Decimal Notation

You can use what you know about place value to help you understand decimals. There are many ways to represent numbers. One way is to use a grid. A second way is to use numbers, and a third way is to use words. A place-value chart like the one at the right can help you understand decimals.

Thousands	Hundreds	Tens	Ones		Tenths	Hundredths	Thousandths
			1	.	2	9	

Grid form:

→

Number form: 1.29

Word form: one and twenty-nine hundredths

▶ Example 1

Write the decimal number represented by the grid.

The grid is divided into 10 sections, so each section represents tenths. Five sections are shaded, so the grid represents 0.5.

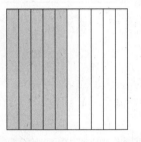

▶ Example 2

Write four and three hundred eleven thousandths as a decimal.

You know that the decimal point is read as "and," so the decimal is 4.311.

MATH SKILLS

Adding and Subtracting Decimal Numbers

hen you add or subtract decimals, first line up the decimal points, and annex zeros if necessary. Then add or subtract as if you were adding or subtracting whole numbers.

▶ Example 1

Add 1.4 and 1.63. Use models, if you like.

Line up the decimal points. Annex zeros so that both numbers have the same number of digits to the right of the decimal point.

Add, beginning with the hundredths.

The sum of 1.4 and 1.63 is 3.03.

$$\begin{array}{r} 1.40 \\ +\ 1.63 \\ \hline 3.03 \end{array}$$

▶ Example 2

Subtract 0.34 from 1.7. Use models, if you like.

Line up the decimal points. Annex zeros so that both numbers have the same number of digits to the right of the decimal point.

Subtract, beginning with the hundredths.

The difference between 1.7 and 0.34 is 1.36.

$$\begin{array}{r} 1.70 \\ -\ 0.34 \\ \hline 1.36 \end{array}$$

Solving Decimal Equations: Add and Subtract

You can solve addition and subtraction equations involving decimals by using mental math. You can also work backward to solve for the variable.

▶ Example

Solve $x + 5.3 = 6.6$.

Step 1: Think: What number plus 5.3 equals 6.6?	$x + 5.3 = 6.6$
Step 2: Use mental math.	$\mathbf{1.3} + 5.3 = 6.6$
Step 3: Check to see that the equation is true.	$6.6 = 6.6 ✓$

You could also work backward to solve for *x*.

Start with the answer and subtract the known addend. $6.6 - 5.3 = 1.3$

In the equation $x + 5.3 = 6.6$, *x* is equal to 1.3.

MATH SKILLS

Scientific Notation

Scientific notation is an easier way to write very large and very small numbers. A number in scientific notation is written as the product of a number between 1 and 10 and a power of 10. You write the power of 10 using exponents, with 10 as the base and the number of times that 10 is a factor as the exponent.

Example 1

Write 4.2×10^7 in standard form.

The power of 10 tells you how many places to move the decimal point. Move the decimal point *to the right* 7 places.

So, $4.2 \times 10^7 = 42,000,000$.

$$4.2 \times 10^7 = 42,000,000$$
7 places

Example 2

Write 7,089,000 in scientific notation.

Write 7,089,000 as a product of two numbers. The first factor is the decimal number with one digit before the decimal. To write this number, move the decimal point *to the left* 6 placcs.

The second factor is a power of 10. The exponent is the number of places the decimal point was moved.

So, $7,089,000 = 7.089 \times 10^6$.

7,089,000
6 places

10^6

Understanding Fractions

A fraction describes part of a whole when the whole is cut into equal pieces. The **numerator,** or top number, tells how many parts are named. The **denominator,** or bottom number, gives the number of parts in the whole.

$\dfrac{2}{3}$ ← numerator
← denominator

Example

What fraction does the shaded part represent?

Find the numerator by counting the number of shaded parts. There are 5 shaded parts, so the numerator is 5.

Find the denominator by counting the total number of parts in the whole. There are 6 parts in the whole, so the denominator is 6.

The fraction is $\frac{5}{6}$.

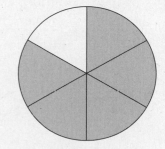

Converting in the Metric System

The **metric system** is a system of measurements used to describe how long, how heavy, or how big something is. The metric system uses **prefixes** to describe amounts that are much larger or smaller than the base unit. The base units for measuring length, mass, and volume are shown in the table below. The prefixes used most often are **kilo-,** meaning 1,000; **centi-,** meaning $\frac{1}{100}$; and **milli-,** meaning $\frac{1}{1,000}$.

To **convert** a unit in the metric system, you need to multiply or divide by a power of 10. The table below lists the powers of 10 to use when converting. When converting to a larger unit, your answer gets smaller. When converting to a smaller unit, your answer gets larger. For example, if you are given a distance in millimeters, it will take fewer centimeters to equal that same distance.

÷ 1,000	÷ 100	÷ 10	base unit	× 10	× 100	× 1,000
kilo-	hecto-	deca-	meter gram liter	deci-	centi-	milli-
× 1,000	× 100	× 10	base unit	÷ 10	÷ 100	÷ 1,000

 ## Example 1

Convert 34,000 milliliters to liters.

You are converting from a smaller unit to a larger unit, so you will divide. Refer to the conversion table to find the divisor. When converting from milliliters to liters, divide by 1,000.

$$34,000 \div 1,000 = 34$$

So, 34,000 milliliters = 34 liters.

Example 2

Convert 72.5 decameters to meters.

You are converting from a larger unit to a smaller unit, so you will multiply. When converting from decameters to meters, multiply by 10.

$$72.5 \times 10 = 725$$

So, 72.5 decameters = 725 meters.

MATH SKILLS

Using Conversion Factors

The customary system is another system of measurement. It is not based on powers of 10. In order to convert from one unit to another, you need to know the **conversion factor,** or the number of units that another unit is equal to.

Length	Weight	Liquid Capacity
1 foot (ft) = 12 inches (in.) 1 yard (yd) = 3 feet (ft) 1 mile (mi) = 5,280 feet (ft)	1 pound (lb) = 16 ounces (oz)	1 gallon (gal) = 4 quarts (qt)

To convert from a larger unit to a smaller unit, you *multiply* by the appropriate conversion factor. To convert from a smaller unit to a larger unit, you *divide* by the appropriate conversion factor.

 ## Example 1

How many feet are in 3 yards?

When you convert from a larger unit (yard) to a smaller unit (foot), multiply the number of yards by the number of feet in a yard.

1 yd = 3 ft

$3 \times 3 = 9$

There are 9 feet in 3 yards.

 ## Example 2

How many feet are in 24 inches?

When you convert from a smaller unit (inches) to a larger unit (feet), divide the number of feet by the number of inches in a foot.

1 ft = 12 in.

$24 \div 12 = 2$

There are 2 feet in 24 inches.

MATH SKILLS

Converting Fractions and Decimals

Fractions and decimals can be used to name the same number. Sometimes it is necessary to write a fraction as a decimal or a decimal as a fraction.

▶ Example 1

To write a fraction as a decimal, divide the numerator by the denominator. Your answer will be a **terminating decimal,** one with no remainder, or a **repeating decimal,** one that repeats a pattern.

a. Write $\frac{2}{5}$ as a decimal.

Divide 2 by 5.

$$
\begin{array}{r}
0.4 \\
5\overline{)2.0} \\
\underline{2\ 0}
\end{array}
$$

The fraction $\frac{2}{5}$ and the decimal 0.4 name the same number.

b. Write $\frac{2}{9}$ as a decimal.

Divide 2 by 9.

$$
\begin{array}{r}
0.222... \\
9\overline{)2.000} \\
\underline{1\ 8} \\
20 \\
\underline{18} \\
20
\end{array}
$$

The fraction $\frac{2}{9}$ and the decimal 0.222… name the same number.

▶ Example 2

To write a terminating decimal as a fraction, write the digits in the decimal as the numerator. Use the place value of the decimal to write the denominator. Then write your answer in lowest terms.

Write 0.3 as a fraction.

$$0.3 = \frac{3}{10} \longleftarrow \text{place value of decimal}$$

The fraction is in lowest terms, so the decimal 0.3 and the fraction $\frac{3}{10}$ name the same number.

MATH SKILLS

Skills and Content Review

An **angle** is formed by two rays with the same endpoint. The rays are the **sides** of the angle. The common endpoint is the **vertex.**

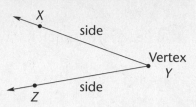

side

X

Vertex
Y

side

Z

You can name an angle using a point on each side and the vertex. The vertex must appear as the middle letter. When it is not confusing, you can name an angle using the vertex alone. The angle shown can be called $\angle XYZ$, $\angle ZYX$, or $\angle Y$.

Angles can be classified by their size.

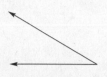

An **acute angle** is smaller than a right angle.

A **right angle** is like the corner of an index card.

An **obtuse angle** is greater than a right angle but smaller than a straight angle.

A **straight angle** is a line.

▶ Example 1

Name the angle in three ways. Identify the vertex.

The angle can be named $\angle UST$, $\angle TSU$, or $\angle S$.

The vertex is S.

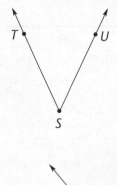

T

U

S

▶ Example 2

Classify $\angle W$ as acute, right, obtuse, or straight.

Since the angle is smaller than a right angle, it is acute.

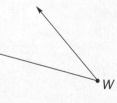

W

MATH SKILLS

Measuring Angles

ngles are measured in units called **degrees.** Use the symbol ° to indicate degrees. A complete circle measures 360°.

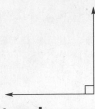

An **acute angle** measures more than 0° and less than 90°.

A **right angle** measures exactly 90°.

An **obtuse angle** measures more than 90° and less than 180°.

A **protractor** is a tool that measures angles.

▶ Example

What is the measure of ∠ FGH?

> *Step 1:* Place your protractor so that the middle mark (hole) on its bottom side is exactly on the vertex of the angle.
>
> *Step 2:* Place the protractor line, zero mark on the scale, over one side of the angle.
>
> *Step 3:* Read the number where the other side of the angle meets the degree scale. Since the angle is an acute angle, use the smaller number in the pair.

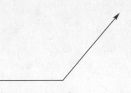

The measure of ∠ FGH is 75°.

Flips and Line Symmetry

Two figures are **congruent** if they have the same size and shape. A figure that can be folded into congruent halves has **line symmetry**. A **reflection** is the mirror image of a figure that has been "flipped" over a line.

▶ Example 1

Draw the reflection of the figure over the line.

Draw the mirror image of the figure.

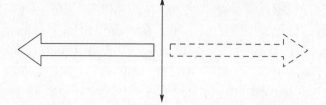

▶ Example 2

Tell if the line is a line of symmetry.

If the figure was folded at the line, the two parts would match exactly. So, the line is a line of symmetry.

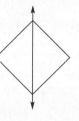

▶ Example 3

Tell if the figures are congruent.

The figures are the same shape, but are different sizes. So, the figures are not congruent.

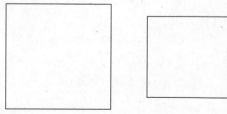

MATH SKILLS

The Coordinate Plane

You can use a **coordinate plane** to locate points on the plane. The **x-axis** and the **y-axis** are number lines. They intersect at right angles at their zero points, the **origin.**

Any point can be located using an **ordered pair.** The first **coordinate** tells you how far to move on the x-axis from the origin. Coordinates of points to the right of the origin are *positive* numbers. Coordinates of points to the left are *negative* numbers. The second coordinate tells you how far to move on the y-axis from the origin. Coordinates of points up from the origin are *positive* numbers. Coordinates of points down from the origin have coordinates that are *negative* numbers.

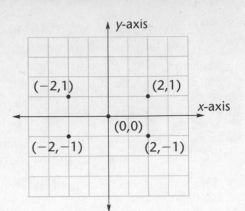

▶ Example 1

Give the coordinates of Point A.

Start at the origin. Go right along the x-axis until you are above Point A. You move 3 units *right*, so the first coordinate is +3, or 3.

Then go down to Point A. You move 2 units *down*, so the second coordinate is −2.

The coordinates of Point A are (3,−2).

▶ Example 2

Plot and label Point G(−4,3)

Start at the origin. Since the first coordinate is negative, go *left* along the x-axis 4 units.

Then, since the second coordinate is positive, go *up* 3 units.

Label the point as G.

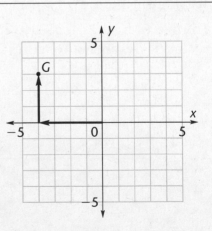

MATH SKILLS

Skills and Content Review

Graphing Equations

You can use the coordinate plane to graph equations with two variables. A **T-table** can show various solutions to an equation.

▶ Example 1

Graph the equation $y = x + 5$.

Step 1: Make a T-table for four values of x and y that will solve the equation.

x	y
−2	3
−1	4
0	5
1	6

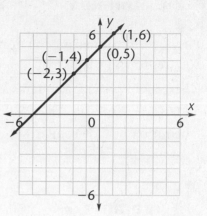

Step 2: Plot the point for each pair of (x, y) values on the coordinate plane.

Step 3: Draw a line connecting the points. This line represents all the other values for x and the matching y values that make the equation true. This line is the graph of the equation $y = x + 5$.

▶ Example 2

Graph the equation $y = 2x$.

First make a table of values.

x	0	1	2	3
y	0	2	4	6

Then graph the ordered pairs (0, 0), (1, 2), (2, 4), and (3, 6). Connect the points.

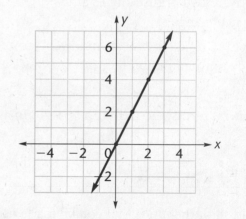

MATH SKILLS

What Is a Ratio?

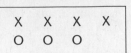

A ratio is a comparison of two quantities. The ratio of Xs to Os in the box can be written as 4 to 3, 4:3, or $\frac{4}{3}$. Like fractions, ratios can be rewritten in lowest terms.

 ## Example 1

Give a ratio comparing the number of shaded squares to white squares.

There are five shaded squares and two white squares.

The ratio of shaded squares to white squares can be written as 5 to 2, 5:2, or $\frac{5}{2}$.

Example 2

Give a ratio comparing the number of obtuse angles to acute angles. Write this ratio in lowest terms.

There are two obtuse angles and four acute angles.

Write the ratio. To rewrite in lowest terms, divide numerator and denominator by the same number.

Simplify.

In lowest terms, the ratio can be written as 1 to 2, 1:2, or $\frac{1}{2}$.

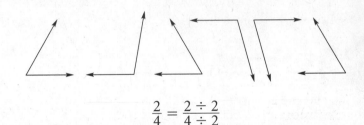

$$\frac{2}{4} = \frac{2 \div 2}{4 \div 2}$$
$$= \frac{1}{2}$$

Example 3

Write all of the ratios that can be made using the figure at the right.

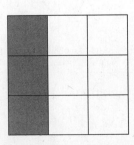

Shaded squares to total squares: 3 to 9 = 1 to 3
Total squares to shaded squares: 9 to 3 = 3 to 1
Unshaded squares to total squares: 6 to 9 = 2 to 3
Total squares to unshaded squares: 9 to 6 = 3 to 2
Shaded squares to unshaded squares: 3 to 6 = 1 to 2
Unshaded squares to shaded squares: 6 to 3 = 2 to 1

MATH SKILLS

What Is a Rate?

Some ratios are known as **rates**. A rate is a comparison of two quantities with different units of measure, such as $\frac{60 \text{ mi}}{1 \text{ hr}}$. If the comparison is to 1 unit, the rate is called a **unit rate**. Find equal rates by multiplying or dividing both quantities by the same number.

 Example 1

State if the ratio $\frac{3 \text{ apples}}{\$5}$ is a rate.

The ratio is a rate because the measures are in different units.

 Example 2

State if the rate 45 students in two classrooms is a unit rate.

The ratio is *not* a unit rate because the comparison is to 2 classrooms. To be a unit rate, the comparison must be to one unit.

Example 3

Ingrid runs 15 miles every 7 days. Use a table to find three more rates describing this situation.

		× 2	× 3	× 4
Miles Run	15	30	45	60
Days	7	14	21	28

Three rates are $\frac{30 \text{ miles}}{14 \text{ days}}$, $\frac{45 \text{ miles}}{21 \text{ days}}$, $\frac{60 \text{ miles}}{28 \text{ days}}$.

Example 4

Stephanie spent $6 for 2 cafeteria lunches at school last week.

Complete the table to find equal ratios for 6:2.

Divide both 6 and 2 by 2. Then multiply both 6 and 2 by 2, 3, 4, and 5.

Cost ($)	3	6	12	18	24	30
Number of lunches	1	2	4	6	8	10

Each column of the table represents a ratio equal to 6:2.

What Is a Proportion?

or two ratios, a **cross product** is the result of multiplying the top value in one ratio by the bottom value in the other.

A **proportion** is a pair of equal ratios. Units of measurement must be the same across the top and bottom *or* down the left and right sides. In a proportion the cross products of the two ratios are equal.

▶ Example 1

Find the cross products for the ratios $\frac{3 \text{ ft}}{5 \text{ sec}}$ and $\frac{12 \text{ ft}}{20 \text{ sec}}$.

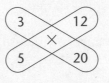

Multiply the top value of the first ratio and the bottom value of the second ratio.

$$3 \times 20 = 60$$

Multiply the bottom value of the first ratio and the top value of the second ratio.

$$5 \times 12 = 60$$

The cross products are 60 and 60.

▶ Example 2

State whether the ratios form a proportion.

Find the cross products for the ratios

$\frac{6 \text{ min}}{3 \text{ min}}$ and $\frac{12 \text{ ft}}{6 \text{ ft}}$.

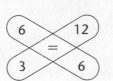

The cross products are equal, so the ratios form a proportion.

MATH SKILLS

Solving Proportions Using Cross Products

If you know one measurement and the ratio that the known and an unknown measurement should have, you can write a proportion. Then you can use mental math or division to find the value of the unknown measure.

▶ Example

Use mental math to solve the proportion $\frac{4}{8} = \frac{3}{a}$.

Write the cross products as an equation. $\quad\quad 4a = 8 \times 3$

Multiply. $\quad\quad\quad\quad\quad\quad\quad\quad\quad\quad 4a = 24$

Think: What number times 4 equals 24? $\quad a = 6$

So, the proportion is $\frac{4}{8} = \frac{3}{6}$.

Solving Proportions Using Unit Rates

A unit rate is a ratio where one quantity is compared to exactly one unit of another quantity. Unit rates can be used to solve proportions. Divide to find the unit rate of the given proportion. Use multiplication to find the unknown value.

▶ Example 1

Find the rate of $\dfrac{\$24}{10 \text{ paintbrushes}}$.

Divide by the unit quantity and simplify. $\quad\quad \dfrac{\$24 \div 10}{10 \text{ paintbrushes} \div 10} = \dfrac{\$2.40}{1 \text{ paintbrush}}$

So, the unit rate is $2.40 for one paintbrush.

▶ Example 2

Use unit rates to solve the proportion $\dfrac{\$60}{12 \text{ pounds}} = \dfrac{?}{15 \text{ pounds}}$.

Divide to find the unit rate. $\quad\quad\quad\quad \dfrac{\$60 \div 12}{12 \text{ pounds} \div 12} = \dfrac{\$5}{1 \text{ pound}}$

Multiply the unit rate by the number of pounds. $\quad$ $5 per pound $\times$ 15 pounds = $75

So, it would cost $75 for 15 pounds.

MATH SKILLS

What Is a Percent?

A **percent** is a ratio that compares a part to a whole using the number 100. The percent is the number of hundredths that the part is equal to.

▶ Example

Give the percent of the figure that is shaded.

45 of the 100 squares are shaded. $\frac{45}{100} = 45\%$

So, 45% of the figure is shaded.

Converting Percents to Fractions and Decimals

F ractions, percents, and decimals all describe parts of a whole. To convert a percent into a fraction or decimal, rewrite the percent as a fraction over 100.

You can use a proportion to convert a fraction into a percent.

$$\frac{\text{part}}{\text{whole}} = \frac{\text{percent value}}{100}$$

▶ Example 1

Convert 15% to a fraction in lowest terms and to a decimal.

Write the percent as a fraction with a denominator of 100.

Then rewrite in requested form.

So, $15\% = \frac{3}{20} = 0.15.$

To convert to a fraction.

$$15\% = \frac{15}{100}$$

$$= \frac{15 \div 5}{100 \div 5} = \frac{3}{20}$$

To convert to a decimal.

$$15\% = \frac{15}{100}$$

$$= 0.15$$

▶ Example 2

Convert $\frac{1}{3}$ to a percent.

Write a proportion using the fraction and 100.

Find the cross products.

Use division to undo multiplication.

Divide. Solve for x.

So, $\frac{1}{3} = 33\frac{1}{3}\%.$

$$\frac{\text{part}}{\text{whole}} \rightarrow \frac{1}{3} = \frac{x}{100} \leftarrow \frac{\text{percent value}}{100}$$

$$100 = 3x$$

$$100 \div 3 = x$$

$$33\frac{1}{3} = x$$

MATH SKILLS

Finding a Percent of a Number

You can use a proportion to find a percent of a whole number or you can convert the percent to a decimal and multiply.

$$\frac{\text{part}}{\text{whole}} = \frac{\text{percent value}}{100}$$

▶ Example

Simplify 22% of 83.

Write a proportion.

Find the cross products.

Use division to undo multiplication.

Divide. Solve for x.

So, 22% of 83 is 18.26.

$$\frac{\text{part}}{\text{whole}} \rightarrow \frac{x}{83} = \frac{22}{100} \leftarrow \frac{\text{percent value}}{100}$$

$$100x = 1826$$

$$x = 1826 \div 100$$

$$x = 18.26$$

Probability

A probability **experiment** is a situation that can happen in more than one way. The **outcomes** of an experiment are the ways it can happen. For example, there are 2 outcomes—a head or a tail—if you toss one coin.

An **event** is the particular outcome that you're looking for. You can describe the **probability** that a particular event will happen by using a ratio.

$$P(\text{event}) = \frac{\text{number of ways the event can happen}}{\text{number of possible outcomes}}$$

It is sometimes helpful to express a probability as a decimal or percent.

▶ Example

Write the probability of spinning A. Then express your answer as a decimal and a percent.

Each section on the spinner represents a letter. All sections are the same size. Therefore, each outcome is equally likely to occur when you spin the spinner.

$P = \frac{1}{4}$ ← Number of ways the event can occur
        ← Possible outcomes: A, B, B, C

$\frac{1}{4} = 0.25$ or 25%

So, the probability of spinning A is $\frac{1}{4}$, 0.25, or 25%.

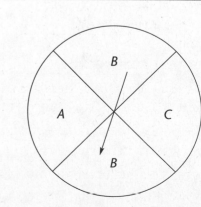

MATH SKILLS

Exploring Surface Area

The **surface area** (*SA*) of a polyhedron is the sum of the areas of all its faces. To find the surface area of a polyhedron, unfold it into a net of polygons and then add their areas. Surface area is measured in square units, such as cm².

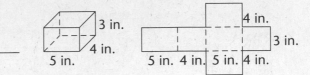

▶ Example

Find the surface area of the prism.

The net consists of 2 rectangles with lengths of 5 in. and widths of 4 in., two 4 in.-by-3 in. rectangles, and two 5 in.-by-3 in. rectangles.

SA = area of 2 rectangles + area of 2 rectangles + area of 2 rectangles

$$
\begin{aligned}
SA &= 2 \times (5 \times 4) &&+ 2 \times (4 \times 3) &&+ 2 \times (5 \times 3) \\
&= 2 \times (20) &&+ 2 \times (12) &&+ 2 \times (15) \\
&= 40 &&+ 24 &&+ 30 &&= 94
\end{aligned}
$$

The surface area of the rectangular prism is 94 in.².

Surface Area Formulas

When a polyhedron has congruent faces, you can use shortcuts (formulas) to find the surface area.

▶ Example 1

Find the surface area of the prism. l = 3 in., w = 5 in., h = 10 in.

Substitute the measures into the formula (shortcut) and solve.

$$
\begin{aligned}
SA &= (2 \times l \times w) + (2 \times l \times h) + (2 \times w \times h) \\
&= (2 \times 3 \times 5) + (2 \times 3 \times 10) + (2 \times 5 \times 10) \\
&= 30 + 60 + 100 \qquad = 190
\end{aligned}
$$

The surface area of the rectangular prism is 190 in.².

▶ Example 2

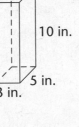

Find the surface area of the pyramid.

The base of the pyramid is a square measuring 4 mm on a side. Each face is a triangle with a base of 4 mm and a height of 6 mm.

Substitute the measures into the formula (shortcut) and solve.

SA (pyramid) = area of base + [(number of triangular faces) × (area of each face)]

$$
\begin{aligned}
&= (4 \times 4) + [4 \times (4 \times 6 \div 2)] \\
&= 16 + [4 \times 12] \qquad = 64
\end{aligned}
$$

The surface area of the pyramid is 64 mm².

MATH SKILLS

Exploring Volume

Three-dimensional objects can be measured by their volume. The **volume** of an object is the number of **cubic units** it contains. You can find the volume of a rectangular prism by counting cubes.

The exponent 3 means to use the base number as a factor 3 times.

5^3 (read "5 cubed") $= 5 \times 5 \times 5 = 125$

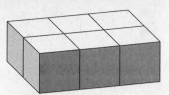

Volume = 6 cubic units

▶ Example

Find the volume of the rectangular prism.

Each layer of the prism is 4 cubes by 5 cubes. This equals 4×5, or 20 cubes.

There are 3 layers in the prism. Multiply the number of layers by the number of cubes in each layer.

$3 \times 20 = 60$ cubes

The volume of the prism is 60 cubic units, or 60 units^3.

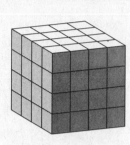

Calculating Volume

You can use a formula to find the volume of a rectangular prism. The volume is the product of the prism's length, width, and height.

> Volume = length × width × height

▶ Example

Find the volume of the rectangular prism.

Find the measure of each dimension.
Length = 10 in. Width = 5 in. Height = 8 in.

Write the formula. $V = l \times w \times h$
Substitute the known values. $V = 10 \times 5 \times 8$
Multiply. $V = 400$

The volume of the prism is 400 cubic inches, or 400 in.^{3}.

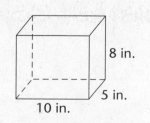

8 in.
5 in.
10 in.

Making Predictions

Sometimes it is difficult to calculate the probability of an event because you don't know all the possible outcomes or you don't know how likely each outcome is. In these situations, you can sometimes collect data and predict the probability based on the data.

A **sample** is a set of data that can be used to predict how a particular situation might happen. You can use sample data to determine probability.

 Example

The school cafeteria manager collected data to see what kind of snacks were chosen most often by the students. Based on this data, what is the probability that students will choose pretzels as a part of their lunch?

Type of snack	Number ordered
Potato	100
Corn	40
Tortilla	80
Cheese puffs	40
Barbecue	60
Pretzels	80

There were 400 bags of snacks chosen. Of the 400 bags, 80 bags were pretzels. So, the manager can expect $\frac{80}{400}$, or $\frac{1}{5}$, of the students to order pretzels.

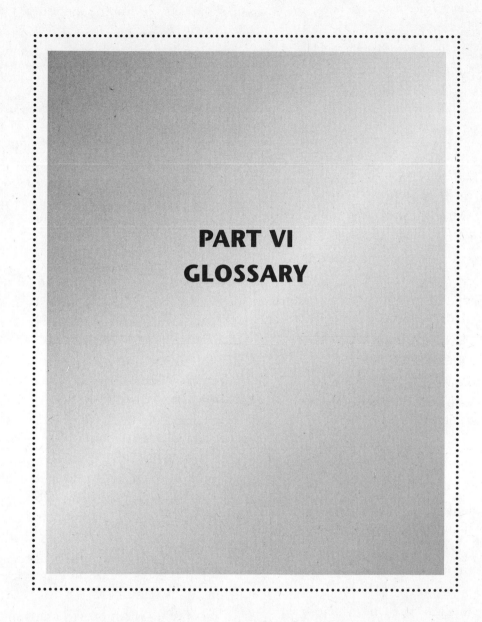

PART VI
GLOSSARY

Glossary

aa A slow-moving type of lava that hardens to form rough chunks; cooler than pahoehoe.

abdomen The hind section of an arachnid's body that contains its reproductive organs and part of its digestive tract; the hind section of an insect's body.

abiotic factor A nonliving part of an ecosystem.

abrasion The grinding away of rock by other rock particles carried in water, ice, or wind.

absolute age The age of a rock given as the number of years since the rock formed.

absolute dating A technique used to determine the actual age of a fossil.

absolute magnitude The brightness of a star if it were a standard distance from Earth.

absolute zero The temperature at which no more energy can be removed from matter.

absorption The process by which nutrient molecules pass through the wall of the digestive system into the blood.

abyssal plain A smooth, nearly flat region of the deep ocean floor.

acceleration The rate at which velocity changes.

accessory pigment A yellow, orange, or red pigment found in plant cells.

acid A substance that tastes sour, reacts with metals and carbonates, and turns blue litmus paper red.

acid rain Rain that is more acidic than normal; caused by the release of molecules of sulfur dioxide and nitrogen oxide into the air.

acne A bacterial infection of the skin in which the oil glands become blocked and swollen.

acoustics The study of how well sounds can be heard in a particular room or hall.

actinide An element in the second row of the rare earth elements in the periodic table.

activation energy The minimum amount of energy needed to start a chemical reaction.

active Said of a volcano that is erupting or has shown signs of erupting in the near future.

active immunity Immunity that occurs when a person's own immune system produces antibodies in response to the presence of a pathogen.

active solar system A method of capturing the sun's energy and distributing it using pumps and fans.

active transport The movement of materials through a cell membrane using energy.

actual mechanical advantage The mechanical advantage that a machine provides in a real situation.

adaptation A characteristic that helps an organism to survive in its environment or to reproduce.

addiction A physical dependence on a substance; an intense need by the body for a substance.

adolescence The stage of development between childhood and adulthood when children become adults physically and mentally.

adrenaline A chemical that gives a burst of energy and causes changes in the body to prepare a person for quick action.

aftershock An earthquake that occurs after a larger earthquake in the same area.

aggression A threatening behavior that one animal uses to gain control over another.

AIDS (acquired immunodeficiency syndrome) A disease caused by a virus that attacks the immune system.

air mass A huge body of air that has similar temperature, pressure, and humidity throughout.

air pollution A change to the atmosphere that has harmful effects.

air pressure A force that is the result of the weight of a column of air pushing down on an area.

air resistance The fluid friction experienced by objects falling through the air.

alcohol A substituted hydrocarbon that contains one or more hydroxyl groups.

GLOSSARY

Skills and Content Review

alcoholism A disease in which a person is both physically addicted to and emotionally dependent on alcohol.

algae Plantlike protists.

algal bloom The rapid growth of a population of algae.

alkali metal An element in Group 1 of the periodic table.

alkaline earth metal An element in Group 2 of the periodic table.

alleles The different forms of a gene.

allergen A substance that causes an allergy.

allergy A disorder in which the immune system is overly sensitive to a foreign substance.

alloy A substance made of two or more elements, at least one of which is a metal, that has the properties of metal.

alluvial fan A wide, sloping deposit of sediment formed where a stream leaves a mountain range.

alpha particle A type of nuclear radiation consisting of two protons and two neutrons.

alternating current Current consisting of charges that move back and forth in a circuit.

altitude Elevation above sea level.

alveoli Tiny sacs of lung tissue specialized for the movement of gases between the air and the blood.

amino acids Small organic compounds that are linked together chemically to form large protein molecules; there are 20 common types of amino acids.

ammeter A device used to measure electric current.

amniocentesis A technique by which a small amount of the fluid that surrounds a developing baby is removed; the fluid is analyzed to determine whether the baby will have a genetic disorder.

amniotic sac A fluid-filled sac that cushions and protects a developing fetus in the uterus.

amorphous solid A solid made up of particles that are not arranged in a regular pattern.

amphibian An ectothermic vertebrate that spends its early life in water and its adulthood on land, returning to water to reproduce.

amplitude The maximum distance the particles of a medium move away from their rest positions as a wave passes through the medium.

amplitude modulation (AM) Method of transmitting radio signals by changing the amplitude of the waves.

anabolic steroids Synthetic chemicals that are similar to hormones produced in the body and that may increase muscle size and cause mood swings.

analog signal An electronic signal in which the current is varied smoothly.

anemometer An instrument used to measure wind speed.

aneroid barometer An instrument that measures changes in air pressure without using a liquid. Changes in the shape of an airtight metal box cause a needle on the barometer dial to move.

angiosperm A plant that produces seeds that are enclosed in a protective structure.

angle of incidence The angle between an incoming wave and an imaginary line drawn perpendicular to the surface of the barrier on the new medium.

angle of reflection The angle between a reflected wave and an imaginary line drawn perpendicular to the surface of the barrier.

antenna An appendage on the head of some animals that contains sense organs.

antibiotic A chemical that kills bacteria or slows their growth without harming the body cells of humans.

antibody A chemical produced by a B cell of the immune system that destroys a specific kind of pathogen.

anticline An upward fold in rock formed by the compression of Earth's crust.

anticyclone A high-pressure center of dry air.

antigen A molecule on a cell that the immune system can recognize either as part of the body or as coming from outside the body.

antinode A point of maximum amplitude on a standing wave.

anus The opening at the end of an organism's digestive system through which wastes exit.

aorta The largest artery in the body.

apparent magnitude The brightness of a star as seen from Earth.

aquaculture The practice of raising fish and other saltwater and freshwater organisms for food.

aquifer An underground layer of rock or soil that holds water.

arachnid An arthropod with only two body sections.

Archimedes' principle The rule that the buoyant force on an object is equal to the weight of the fluid displaced by that object.

armature The moving part of an electric motor, consisting of dozens or hundreds of loops of wire wrapped around an iron core.

artery A blood vessel that carries blood away from the heart.

artesian well A well in which water rises because of pressure within the aquifer.

arthropod An invertebrate that has an external skeleton, a segmented body, and jointed attachments called appendages.

artificial intelligence The capacity of a computer to perform complex tasks such as learning from experience and solving problems.

asexual reproduction The reproductive process that involves only one parent and produces offspring that are identical to the parent.

asteroid belt The region of the solar system between the orbits of Mars and Jupiter, where many asteroids are found.

asteroids Objects revolving around the sun that are too small and too numerous to be considered planets.

asthenosphere The soft layer of the mantle on which the lithosphere floats.

asthma A disorder in which the respiratory passages narrow significantly.

astronomer A scientist who studies the universe beyond Earth.

astronomy The study of the moon, stars, and other objects in space.

atherosclerosis A condition in which an artery wall thickens as a result of the buildup of fatty materials.

atmosphere The mixture of gases that surrounds Earth; the outermost of the four spheres into which scientists divide Earth.

atoll A ring-shaped coral island found far from land.

atom The smallest particle of an element.

atomic mass The average mass of one atom of an element.

atomic mass unit (amu) A unit of measurement for the mass of particles in atoms.

atomic number The number of protons in the nucleus of an atom.

atrium Each of two upper chambers that receives blood that comes into the heart.

aurora A glowing region produced by the interaction of charged particles from the sun and atoms in the atmosphere.

aurora borealis A colorful, glowing display in the sky caused when particles from the sun strike oxygen and nitrogen atoms in the ionosphere; also called the Northern Lights.

autonomic nervous system The group of nerves that controls involuntary actions.

autotroph An organism that makes its own food.

autumnal equinox The day of the year that marks the beginning of fall in the Northern Hemisphere.

auxin The plant hormone that speeds up the rate of growth of plant cells.

GLOSSARY

axis An imaginary line that passes through Earth's center and the North and South poles, about which Earth rotates.

axon A threadlike extension of a neuron that carries nerve impulses away from the cell body.

B cell A lymphocyte that produces chemicals that help destroy a specific kind of pathogen.

bacteriophage A virus that infects bacteria.

bacterium A single-celled organism that is a prokaryote and belongs to one of the two kingdoms—Archaebacteria or Eubacteria.

balanced forces Equal forces acting on an object in opposite directions.

barometer An instrument used to measure changes in air pressure.

basalt A dark, dense, igneous rock with a fine texture, found in oceanic crust.

base A substance that tastes bitter, feels slippery, and turns red litmus paper blue.

base-isolated building A building mounted on bearings designed to absorb the energy of an earthquake.

batholith A mass of rock formed when a large body of magma cooled inside the crust.

battery A combination of two or more electrochemical cells in series.

beach Wave-washed sediment along a coast.

beats The regular changes in loudness of a sound when two sounds of different frequencies are played together.

bedrock The solid layer of rock beneath the soil.

behavior All the actions an animal performs.

benthos Organisms that live on the bottom of the ocean or other body of water.

Bernoulli's principle The rule that a stream of fast-moving fluid exerts less pressure than the surrounding fluid.

beta particle An electron that is given off by a nucleus during radioactive decay.

big bang The initial explosion that resulted in the formation and expansion of the universe.

bilateral symmetry Line symmetry; the quality of being divisible into two halves that are mirror images.

bile A substance produced by the liver that breaks up fat particles.

bimetallic strip A strip made of two different metals that expand at different rates.

binary fission A form of asexual reproduction in which one cell divides to form two identical cells.

binary star A star system that contains two stars.

binary system A number system using combinations of only two digits, 0 and 1; used by computers.

binomial nomenclature The naming system for organisms in which each organism is given a two-part name—a genus name and a species name.

biodegradable Capable of being broken down by bacteria and other natural decomposers.

biodiversity The number of different species in an area.

biogeography The study of where organisms live.

bioluminescence The production of light by a living organism.

biomass The living or formerly living material in an ecosystem.

biomass fuel Fuel made from things that once were alive.

biome A group of ecosystems with similar climates and organisms.

biosphere All living things. One of the four spheres into which scientists divide Earth.

biotic factor A living part of an ecosystem.

bird An endothermic vertebrate that has feathers and a four-chambered heart, and lays eggs.

birthrate The number of births in a population in a certain amount of time.

bit Each binary digit, 1 or 0, in the binary system.

bivalve A mollusk that has two shells held together by hinges and strong muscles.

black hole The remains of an extremely massive star pulled into a small volume by the force of gravity.

blood pressure The pressure that is exerted by the blood against the walls of blood vessels.

blood transfusion The transference of blood from one person to another.

bog A wetland where sphagnum moss grows on top of acidic water.

boiling Vaporization that occurs on and below the surface of a liquid.

boiling point The temperature at which a substance changes from a liquid into a gas.

Boyle's law The relationship between the pressure and volume of a gas at constant temperature; when volume increases, pressure decreases.

brackish water Water that is partly salty and partly fresh, characteristic of estuaries.

brain The part of the central nervous system that is located in the skull and controls most functions in the body.

brainstem The part of the brain that controls many body functions that occur automatically.

branching tree A diagram that shows how scientists think different groups of organisms are related.

bronchi The passages that branch from the trachea and direct air into the lungs.

bronchitis An irritation of the breathing passages in which the small passages become narrower than normal and may be clogged with mucus.

brushes The contact points connected to a current source and the commutator of a motor.

budding A form of asexual reproduction in which a new organism grows out of the body of a parent.

buoyant force The upward force exerted by a fluid on a submerged object.

byte Arrangement of eight bits.

caldera The large hole at the top of a volcano formed when the roof of a volcano's magma chamber collapses.

calorie The amount of energy needed to raise the temperature of one gram of water by one Celsius degree.

cambium The layer of cells in a plant that produces new phloem and xylem cells.

camera Optical instrument that uses lenses to focus light and record an image of an object.

camouflage Protective coloration; a common animal defense.

cancer A disease in which some body cells grow and divide uncontrollably, damaging the parts of the body around them.

canines Sharply pointed teeth that stab food and tear into it.

canopy A leafy roof formed by tall trees.

capillary A tiny blood vessel where substances are exchanged between the blood and the body cells.

capillary action The combined force of attraction among water molecules and with the molecules of surrounding materials.

captive breeding The mating of endangered animals in zoos or preserves.

carbohydrate Energy-rich organic compounds, such as sugars and starches, that are made of the elements carbon, hydrogen, and oxygen. Carbohydrates are a major source of energy and provide the raw materials to make parts of cells.

carbon film A type of fossil consisting of an extremely thin coating of carbon on rock.

carbon monoxide A colorless, odorless gas produced when substances—including tobacco—are burned.

carboxyl group A group of atoms, -COOH group, found in organic acids.

carcinogen A substance or a factor in the environment that can cause cancer.

cardiac muscle Muscle tissue found only in the heart.

cardiovascular system The body system that consists of the heart, blood vessels, and blood, and that carries needed substances to cells and carries waste products away from cells.

carnivore An animal that eats only other animals.

carrier A person who has one recessive allele for a trait and one dominant allele, but does not have the trait.

GLOSSARY

carrying capacity The largest population that an area can support.

cartilage A connective tissue that is more flexible than bone and that gives support to some parts of the body.

cast A fossil that is a copy of an organism's shape, formed when minerals seep into a mold.

catalyst A material that increases the rate of a chemical reaction by lowering the activation energy.

catalytic converter A device that reduces carbon monoxide emissions from vehicles.

cathode-ray tube (CRT) A sealed glass vacuum tube that uses electrons to produce images on a screen; picture tube.

cell The basic unit of structure and function in living things.

cell cycle The regular sequence of growth and division that cells undergo.

cell membrane The outside boundary of a cell; the cell membrane controls which substances can enter or leave the cell.

cell theory A widely accepted explanation of the relationship between cells and living things.

cell wall A rigid layer of nonliving material that surrounds the cells of plants and some other organisms.

cellulose A complex carbohydrate with which plants build strong stems and roots.

Celsius scale The temperature scale on which zero and 100 are the temperatures at which water freezes and boils.

cementation The process by which dissolved minerals crystallize and glue particles of sediment together into one mass.

central nervous system The brain and spinal cord; the control center of the body.

central processing unit (CPU) The part of a computer that directs the operation of the computer.

centripetal force A force that causes an object to move in a circle.

cephalopod A mollusk with feet adapted to form tentacles around its mouth.

ceramic A hard, crystalline solid made by heating clay and other mineral materials to high temperatures.

cerebellum The part of the brain that coordinates the actions of the muscles and helps maintain balance.

cerebrum The part of the brain that interprets input from the senses, controls the movement of skeletal muscles, and carries out complex mental processes.

change of state The physical change of matter from one state to another.

characteristic property A quality of a substance that never changes and can be used to identify the substance.

Charles's law The relationship between the temperature and volume of a gas at constant pressure; when temperature increases, volume increases.

chat room A network feature that allows two or more computer users to exchange messages.

chemical activity A characteristic property of a substance that indicates its ability to undergo a chemical change.

chemical bond The force that holds atoms together.

chemical change A change in matter that produces new substances.

chemical digestion The process that breaks large food molecules into smaller molecules.

chemical energy The potential energy stored in chemical bonds.

chemical equation A short, easy way to show chemical reactions, using symbols instead of words.

chemical formula A combination of symbols that represents the elements in a compound.

chemical property A characteristic that is observed when a substance interacts with another substance.

Glossary

chemical reaction A process in which substances undergo chemical changes.

chemical rock Sedimentary rock that forms when minerals crystallize from a solution.

chemical symbol A one- or two-letter representation of an element.

chemical weathering The process that breaks down rock through chemical changes.

chemistry The study of the properties of matter and how matter changes.

chemotherapy The use of drugs to kill cancer cells.

chitin The tough, flexible material from which arthropod exoskeletons are made.

chlorofluorocarbons (CFCs) Chlorine compounds formerly used in air conditioners, refrigerators, and spray cans.

chlorophyll A green pigment found in the chloroplasts of plants, algae, and some compounds.

chloroplast A structure in the cells of plants and some other organisms that captures energy from light and uses it to produce food.

cholesterol A waxy, fatlike substance, found only in animal cells, that is an important part of body cells; can build up on artery walls.

chordate The phylum whose members have a notochord, a nerve cord, and slits in their throat area at some point in their lives.

chromatid One of the identical rods of a chromosome.

chromatin Material in cells that contains DNA and carries genetic information.

chromosome A rod-shaped cellular structure made of condensed chromatin; contains DNA, which carries the genetic information that controls inherited characteristics such as eye color and blood type.

chromosphere The middle layer of the sun's atmosphere.

cilia The hairlike projections on the outside of cells that move in a wavelike manner.

cinder cone A steep, cone-shaped hill or mountain made of volcanic ash, cinders, and bombs piled up around a volcano's opening.

circadian rhythms Behavior cycles that occur over a period of approximately one day.

circuit breaker A safety device that uses an electromagnet to shut off a circuit when the current becomes too high.

cirrus Wispy, feathery clouds made mostly of ice crystals that form at high levels, above about 6 kilometers.

classification The process of grouping things based on their similarities.

clastic rock Sedimentary rock that forms when rock fragments are squeezed together under high pressure.

clear-cutting The process of cutting down all the trees in an area at once.

cleavage A mineral's ability to split easily along flat surfaces.

climate The average, year-after-year conditions of temperature, precipitation, winds, and clouds in an area.

clone An organism that is genetically identical to the organism from which it was produced.

cnidarians Animals whose stinging cells are used to capture their prey and defend themselves, and who take their food into a hollow central cavity.

coagulation The process by which particles in a liquid clump together; a step in the water treatment process.

cochlea A snail-shaped tube in the inner ear lined with sound receptors; nerve impulses are sent from the cochlea to the brain.

codominance A condition in which neither of two alleles of a gene is dominant or recessive.

coefficient A number in front of a chemical formula in an equation that indicates how many molecules or atoms of each reactant and product are involved in a reaction.

colloid A mixture with small undissolved particles that do not settle out.

GLOSSARY

combustion A rapid reaction between oxygen and fuel that results in fire; burning a fuel produces thermal energy.

comet A ball of ice and dust whose orbit is a long, narrow ellipse.

commensalism A relationship between two species in which one species benefits and the other is neither helped nor harmed.

community All the different populations that live together in an area.

commutator A device that controls the direction of the flow of current through an electric motor.

compaction The process by which sediments are pressed together under their own weight.

compass A device with a magnetized needle that can spin freely; a compass needle always points north.

competition The struggle between organisms for the limited resources in a habitat.

complementary colors Any two colors that combine to form white light or black pigment.

complete metamorphosis A type of meta-morphosis characterized by four dramatically different stages: egg, larva, pupa, and adult.

complex carbohydrate A substance consisting of long chains of simple carbohydrates.

composite A combination of two or more substances that creates a new material.

composite volcano A tall, cone-shaped mountain in which layers of lava alternate with layers of ash and other volcanic materials.

composting Helping the natural decomposition process to break down certain wastes.

compound A substance made of two or more elements chemically combined.

compound machine A device that combines two or more simple machines.

compound microscope A light microscope that has more than one lens.

compression (1) Stress that squeezes rock until it folds or breaks. (2) The part of a longitudinal wave where the particles of the medium are close together.

computer An electronic device that stores, processes, and retrieves information.

computer hardware The permanent components of a computer, including the central processing unit and input, output, and memory storage devices.

computer network A group of computers connected by cables or telephone lines that allows people to share information.

computer programmer A person who uses computer languages to convert input information into instructions that a computer can understand.

computer software A detailed set of instructions that directs the computer hardware to perform operations on stored information.

computer virus A program that interferes with the normal operation of a computer.

concave lens A lens that is thinner in the center than at the edges.

concave mirror A mirror with a surface that curves inward.

concentrated solution A mixture that has a lot of solute dissolved in it.

concentration The amount of one material dissolved in a given amount of another material.

concussion A bruiselike injury of the brain that occurs when the soft tissue of the cerebrum bumps against the skull.

condensation The process by which a gas, such as water vapor, changes into a liquid, such as water.

conditioning The process of learning to connect a stimulus with a good or bad event.

conduction The transfer of heat, or thermal energy, from one substance to another by direct contact of particles of matter. Also, the transfer of electrons from a charged object to another object.

conductor A substance through which electrons move freely, transmitting heat or electricity.

cone (1) The reproductive structure of a gymnosperm. (2) A cell on the retina that detects color.

GLOSSARY

Glossary

coniferous trees Trees that produce their seeds in cones and have needle-shaped leaves.

conjugation The process in which a unicellular organism transfers some of its genetic material to another unicellular organism.

connective tissue A body tissue that provides support for the body and connects all of its parts.

conservation The process of using a resource wisely so it will not be used up.

conservation of charge The law that states that charges are neither created nor destroyed.

conservation of mass The principle stating that matter is not created or destroyed during a chemical reaction.

conservation plowing Soil conservation method in which the dead stalks from the previous year's crop are left in the ground to hold the soil in place.

conservation viewpoint The belief that people should use natural resources as long as they do not destroy those resources.

constellation A pattern of stars in the sky.

constructive force A force that builds up mountains and landmasses on Earth's surface.

constructive interference The interference that occurs when two waves combine to make a wave with a larger amplitude.

consumer An organism that obtains energy by feeding on other organisms.

continent A great landmass surrounded by oceans.

continental air mass A dry air mass that forms over land.

continental climate The climate of the centers of continents, with cold winters and warm or hot summers.

continental drift The hypothesis that the continents slowly move across Earth's surface.

continental glacier A glacier that covers much of a continent or large island.

continental shelf A gently sloping, shallow area of the ocean floor that extends outward from the edge of a continent.

continental slope An incline leading down from the edge of the continental shelf.

continuum A gradual progression through many stages between one extreme and another, as in the illness-wellness continuum.

contour feather A large feather that helps give shape to a bird's body.

contour interval The difference in elevation from one contour line to the next.

contour line A line on a topographic map that connects points of equal elevation.

contour plowing Plowing fields along the curves of a slope to prevent soil loss.

contractile vacuole The cell structure that collects extra water from the cytoplasm and then expels it from the cell.

control rod Cadmium rod used in a nuclear reactor to absorb neutrons from fission.

controlled experiment An experiment in which all factors except one are kept constant.

convection The transfer of heat by the movement of a fluid.

convection current (1) The movement of a fluid, caused by differences in temperature, that transfers heat from one part of the fluid to another. (2) A current caused by the rising of heated fluid and sinking of cooled fluid.

convergent boundary A plate boundary where two plates move toward each other.

convex lens A lens that is thicker in the center than at the edges.

convex mirror A mirror with a surface that curves outward.

coral reef A structure of calcite shells built up by coral animals living in warm, shallow ocean water.

core (1) The central part of the sun, where nuclear fusion occurs. (2) The dense center of Earth, consisting of a solid inner core and a hot, liquid outer core.

Coriolis effect The way Earth's rotation makes winds and currents in the Northern Hemisphere curve to the right and winds in the Southern Hemisphere curve to the left.

Glossary

cornea The clear tissue that covers the front of the eye.

corona The outer layer of the sun's atmosphere.

coronary artery An artery that supplies blood to the heart itself.

corrosion The gradual wearing away of a metal element due to a chemical reaction.

corrosive Able to dissolve or break down many other substances; strong acids are corrosive.

cotyledon A seed leaf that stores food.

courtship behavior The behavior that animals of the same species engage in to prepare for mating.

covalent bond A chemical bond formed when two atoms share electrons.

crater (1) A bowl-shaped area that forms around a volcano's central opening. (2) A round pit on the surface of a moon or planet caused by a meteoroid.

crest The highest point of a transverse wave.

crop A bird's internal storage tank that allows it to store food inside its body after swallowing it.

crop rotation The planting of different crops in a field each year.

crust The layer of rock that forms Earth's outer surface.

crustacean An arthropod that has two or three body sections, five or more pairs of legs, two pairs of antennae, and usually three pairs of appendages for chewing.

crystal A solid in which atoms or ions are arranged in a three-dimensional pattern that repeats again and again.

crystalline solid A substance that is made up of crystals in which particles are arranged in a regular, repeating pattern.

cumulus Clouds that form less than 2 kilometers above the ground and look like fluffy, rounded piles of cotton.

current A large stream of moving water that flows through the ocean.

cuticle The waxy, waterproof layer that covers the leaves and stems of some plants.

cyclone A swirling center of low air pressure.

cytokinesis The final stage of the cell cycle, in which the cell's cytoplasm divides, distributing the organelles into each of the two new cells.

cytoplasm The region of a cell located inside the cell membrane (in prokaryotes) or between the cell membrane and nucleus (in eukaryotes); contains a gel-like material and cell organelles.

data The facts, figures, and other evidence gained through observation.

death rate The number of deaths in a population in a certain amount of time.

decibel (dB) A unit of measurement of loudness.

deciduous trees Trees that shed their leaves and grow new ones each year.

decomposer An organism that breaks down large chemicals from dead organisms into small chemicals and returns important materials to the soil and water.

decomposition A chemical reaction that breaks down compounds into simpler products.

deep-ocean trench A deep valley along the ocean floor through which oceanic crust slowly sinks toward the mantle.

deflation Wind erosion that removes surface materials.

deformation A change in the volume or shape of Earth's crust.

degree (1) A unit used to measure distances around a circle. One degree equals 1/360 of a full circle. (2) A division of a temperature scale.

delivery The second stage of birth, in which the baby is pushed completely out of the uterus, through the vagina, and out of the mother's body.

delta A landform made of sediment that is deposited where a river flows into an ocean or lake.

Glossary

dendrite A threadlike extension of a neuron that carries nerve impulses toward the cell body.

density The measurement of how much mass of a substance is contained in a given volume.

deposition The process by which sediment settles out of the water or wind that is carrying it and is deposited in a new location.

depressant A drug that slows down the activity of the central nervous system.

dermis The lower layer of the skin.

desalination The process of obtaining fresh water from salt water by removing the salt.

desert (1) A region that gets fewer than 25 centimeters of rain a year. (2) An area in which the yearly amount of evaporation is greater than the amount of precipitation.

desertification The advance of desertlike conditions into areas that previously were fertile.

destructive force A force that slowly wears away mountains and other features on the surface of Earth.

destructive interference The interference that occurs when two waves combine to make a wave with a smaller amplitude.

development (1) The construction of buildings, roads, dams, and other structures. (2) The process of change that occurs during an organism's life to produce a more complex organism.

development viewpoint The belief that humans should be able to freely use and benefit from all of Earth's resources.

dew point The temperature at which condensation begins.

diabetes A condition in which either the pancreas fails to produce enough insulin, or the body's cells can't use it properly.

diamond A form of the element carbon; it is the hardest mineral crystal on Earth.

diaphragm A large, dome-shaped muscle in a mammal's chest that plays an important role in breathing.

diatomic molecule A molecule composed of two atoms.

dicot An angiosperm that has two seed leaves.

diffraction The bending of waves around the edge of a barrier.

diffuse reflection Reflection that occurs when parallel rays of light hit a rough surface and all reflect at different angles.

diffusion The process by which molecules move from an area in which they are highly concentrated to an area in which they are less concentrated.

digestion The process by which the body breaks down food into small nutrient molecules.

digital signal An electronic signal in which the current is varied in steps.

digitizing Converting information to numbers for use by a computer.

dike A slab of volcanic rock formed when magma forces itself across rock layers.

dilute solution A mixture that has little solute dissolved in it.

diode A solid-state component that consists of layers of semiconductors that allow current to flow in only one direction.

direct current Current consisting of charges that flow in only one direction in a circuit.

directly proportional A term used to describe the relationship between two variables whose graph is a straight line passing through the point (0,0).

disk drive A device that reads information from a disk or enters information onto a disk for a computer.

diskette A plastic disk that holds information and can be removed from the computer.

dislocation An injury in which a bone comes out of its joint.

dispersal The movement of organisms from one place to another.

dissonance The sound produced when notes that have no musical relationship are played together.

GLOSSARY

Skills and Content Review

Glossary

divergent boundary A plate boundary where two plates move away from each other.

divide A ridge of land that separates one watershed, or drainage basin, from another.

DNA Deoxyribonucleic acid; the genetic material that carries information about an organism and is passed from parent to offspring.

dominant allele An allele whose trait always shows up in the organism when the allele is present.

Doppler effect The apparent change in frequency of a sound as the source moves in relation to the listener.

dormant Said of a volcano that does not show signs of erupting in the near future.

double bond A chemical bond formed when two atoms share two pairs of electrons.

down feathers Short, fluffy feathers that trap heat and keep a bird warm.

drainage basin The land area from which a river and its tributaries collect their water.

drought A water shortage caused by long periods of low precipitation in a particular area.

drug Any chemical that causes changes in a person's body or behavior.

drug abuse The deliberate misuse of drugs for purposes other than appropriate medical ones.

dry cell An electrochemical cell in which the electrolyte is a paste.

ductile A term used to describe a material that can be pulled into a long wire.

Dust Bowl The area of the Great Plains where wind erosion caused soil loss during the 1930s.

ear canal A narrow region leading from the outside of the human ear to the eardrum.

eardrum The small, tightly stretched, drumlike membrane that separates the outer ear from the middle ear, and that vibrates when sound waves strike it.

Earth science The science that focuses on planet Earth and its place in the universe.

earthquake The shaking that results from the movement of rock beneath Earth's surface.

echinoderm A radially symmetrical invertebrate that lives on the ocean floor and has a spiny internal skeleton.

echolocation The use of reflection of sound waves to navigate and to locate prey.

eclipse The partial or total blocking of one object by another.

eclipsing binary A star system in which one star periodically blocks the light from another.

ecology The study of how living things interact with each other and their environment.

ecosystem All the living and nonliving things that interact in an area.

ectotherm An animal whose body does not produce much internal heat.

efficiency The percentage of the input work that is converted to output work.

egg A female sex cell.

El Niño An event that occurs every two to seven years in the Pacific Ocean, causing changes in winds, currents, and weather patterns that can cause dramatic climate changes.

elastic potential energy The energy of stretched or compressed objects.

elasticity The ability of a material to bounce back after being disturbed.

electric charge A property of electrons and protons; electrons carry a negative charge, and protons carry a positive charge.

electric circuit A complete path through which electric charges can flow.

electric current The flow of electric charges through a material.

electric field The region around charged particles through which a force is exerted.

electric generator A device that converts mechanical energy into electrical energy.

electric motor A device that converts electrical energy to mechanical energy to turn an axle.

GLOSSARY

electrical energy The energy of moving electrical charges.

electrical potential The potential energy per unit of electric charge.

electrochemical cell A device that converts chemical energy into electrical energy.

electrode A metal strip that gains or loses electrons during electrolysis.

electrolysis A process by which an electric current breaks chemical bonds.

electrolyte A liquid or paste that conducts electricity.

electromagnet A solenoid with a ferromagnetic core that forms a magnet that can be turned on and off.

electromagnetic energy The energy of light and other forms of radiation.

electromagnetic induction The process of generating an electric current from the motion of a conductor through a magnetic field.

electromagnetic radiation Energy that travels through space in the form of electromagnetic waves.

electromagnetic spectrum The range of electromagnetic waves placed in a certain order.

electromagnetic wave Transverse waves that transfer electric and magnetic energy; can travel through space.

electron A tiny, negatively charged, high-energy particle that moves in the space outside the nucleus of an atom.

electron dot diagram A representation of the number of valence electrons in an atom, using dots placed around the symbol of an element.

electronic signal A varying electric current that carries information.

electronics The use of electricity to control, communicate, and process information.

electroscope An instrument used to detect electric charge.

element A substance composed of a single kind of atom. Elements cannot be broken down

into other substances by chemical or physical means.

elevation Height above sea level.

ellipse An elongated circle, or oval shape; the shape of the planets' orbits.

elliptical galaxy A galaxy shaped like a flattened ball, containing only old stars.

embryo (1) A developing human during the first eight weeks after fertilization has occurred. (2) A young plant that develops from a zygote.

emigration Leaving a population.

emissions Particles and gases released into the air from a smokestack or motor vehicle.

emphysema A serious disease that destroys lung tissue and causes difficulty in breathing.

encryption A process of coding information so that only the intended user can read it.

endangered species A species in danger of becoming extinct in the near future.

endocrine gland An organ of the endocrine system which produces and releases its chemical products directly into the bloodstream.

endoplasmic reticulum A cell structure that forms a maze of passageways in which proteins and other materials are carried from one part of the cell to another.

endoskeleton An internal skeleton.

endospore A small, rounded, thick-walled, resting cell that forms inside a bacterial cell.

endotherm An animal whose body controls and regulates its temperature by controlling the internal heat it produces.

endothermic reaction A chemical reaction that absorbs energy in the form of heat.

energy The ability to do work or cause change; for example, to move an object some distance.

energy conservation The practice of reducing energy use.

energy conversion The process of changing one form of energy into another.

energy pyramid A diagram that shows the amount of energy that moves from one feeding level to another in a food web.

energy transformation Any change from one form of energy to another

environmental scientists Scientists who study the effects of human activities on Earth's land, air, water, and living things and also try to solve problems relating to the use of resources.

enzyme (1) A protein that speeds up chemical reactions in the bodies of living things. (2) A biological catalyst that lowers the activation energy of reactions in cells.

epicenter The point on Earth's surface directly above an earthquake's focus.

epidermis The outermost layer of the skin.

epiglottis A flap of tissue that seals off the windpipe and prevents food from entering.

epithelial tissue A body tissue that covers the surfaces of the body, inside and out.

epochs Subdivisions of the periods of the geologic time scale.

equator An imaginary line that circles Earth halfway between the North and South poles.

equilibrium A state in which opposing forces in a system are equally balanced or stable.

equinox The two days of the year on which neither hemisphere is tilted toward or away from the sun.

era One of the three long units of geologic time between the Precambrian and the present.

erosion The process by which water, ice, wind, or gravity moves fragments of rock or soil.

esophagus A muscular tube that connects the mouth to the stomach.

ester An organic compound made by chemically combining an alcohol and an organic acid.

estimate An approximation of a number based on reasonable assumptions.

estrogen A hormone produced by the ovaries that controls the development of adult female characteristics.

estuary A coastal inlet or bay where fresh water from rivers mixes with salty ocean water.

eukaryote An organism with cells that contain nuclei and other cell structures.

eutrophication The process by which nutrients in a lake build up over time, causing an increase in the growth of algae.

evacuate To move away temporarily.

evaporation The process by which molecules at the surface of a liquid absorb enough energy to change to a gaseous state.

evolution The gradual change in a species over time.

excretion The process by which wastes are removed from the body.

exoskeleton An outer skeleton.

exosphere The outer layer of the thermosphere, extending outward into space.

exothermic reaction A chemical reaction that releases energy in the form of heat.

exotic species Species that are carried to a new location by people.

explosive Capable of reacting very quickly when exposed to air or water or when dropped.

external combustion engine An engine powered by fuel burned outside the engine.

external stimulus A change in an organism's surroundings that causes the organism to react.

extinct (1) Term used to describe a species that does not have any living members. (2) Term used to describe a volcano that is unlikely to erupt again.

extinction The disappearance of all members of a species from Earth.

extraterrestrial life Life that arises outside of Earth.

extrusion An igneous rock layer formed when lava flows onto Earth's surface and hardens.

extrusive rock Igneous rock that forms from lava on Earth's surface.

eyepiece A lens that magnifies the image formed by the objective lens.

GLOSSARY

Glossary

Fahrenheit scale The temperature scale on which 32 and 212 are the temperatures at which water freezes and boils.

fallow Left unplanted with crops.

family Elements in the same vertical column of the periodic table. Also called a group.

farsightedness The condition in which distant objects can be seen clearly but nearby objects look blurry.

fats High-energy nutrients that are composed of carbon, oxygen, and hydrogen and contain more than twice as much energy as an equal amount of carbohydrates.

fatty acid An organic compound that is a part of a fat or oil.

fault A break or crack in Earth's lithosphere along which the rocks move.

fault-block mountain A mountain that forms where a normal fault uplifts a block of rock.

fermentation The process by which cells break down molecules to release energy without using oxygen.

ferromagnetic material A material that is strongly attracted to a magnet, and which can be made into a magnet.

fertilization The joining of a sperm cell and an egg cell.

fertilizer A chemical that provides nutrients to help crops grow better.

fetus A developing human from the ninth week of development until birth.

fever An above-normal body temperature that is part of the inflammatory response.

fiber A complex carbohydrate, found in plant foods, that cannot be broken down into sugar molecules by the body.

fibrin A chemical that is important in blood clotting because it forms a fiber net that traps red blood cells.

filtration The process of passing water through a series of screens that allow the water through, but not larger solid particles.

fish An ectothermic vertebrate that lives in the water and has fins.

fishery An area with a large population of valuable ocean organisms.

flagellum A long, whiplike structure that helps a unicellular organism move.

flammable Capable of catching fire easily and burning.

flash flood A sudden, violent flood that occurs within a few hours, or even minutes, of a heavy rainstorm.

flocs Sticky globs created by adding a chemical such as alum during water treatment.

flood The overflowing of a river's channel due to the increase in the volume of the water in the river.

flood plain A broad, flat valley through which a river flows.

flower The reproductive structure of an angiosperm.

fluid Any substance that can flow and easily change shape.

fluid friction Friction that occurs as an object moves through a fluid.

fluorescence The property of a mineral in which the mineral glows under ultraviolet light.

fluorescent lights Lights that glow when an electric current causes ultraviolet waves to strike a coating inside a tube.

focal point The point at which rays of light meet, or appear to meet, after being reflected (or refracted) by a mirror (or a lens).

focus The point beneath Earth's surface where rock breaks under stress and causes an earthquake.

fold A bend in rock that forms where part of Earth's crust is compressed.

foliated Term used to describe metamorphic rocks whose grains are arranged in parallel layers or bands.

GLOSSARY

Skills and Content Review

follicle Structure in the dermis of the skin from which a strand of hair grows.

food chain A series of events in which one organism eats another.

Food Guide Pyramid A chart that classifies foods into six groups to help people plan a healthy diet.

food web The pattern of overlapping food chains in an ecosystem; indicates the feeding relationships in a habitat.

footwall The block of rock that forms the lower half of a fault.

force A push or pull exerted on an object.

formula A combination of symbols that shows the ratio of elements in a compound.

fossil The preserved remains or traces of an organism that lived in the past.

fossil fuel An energy-rich substance, such as coal, oil, or natural gas, formed from the remains of organisms; fossil fuels are burned to release their chemical energy.

fossil record The millions of fossils that scientists have collected.

fracture (1) A break in a bone. (2) The way a mineral looks when it breaks apart in an irregular way.

free fall The motion of a falling object when the only force acting on it is gravity.

freeware Software that the author has decided to let others use free of charge.

freezing The change in state from a liquid to a solid.

freezing point The temperature at which a substance changes from a liquid to a solid.

frequency The number of complete waves that pass a given point in a certain amount of time.

frequency modulation (FM) Method of transmitting radio signals by changing the frequency of the waves.

friction The force that opposes the motion of one surface as it moves across another surface.

frond The leaf of a fern plant.

front The area where air masses meet and do not mix.

fruit The ripened ovary and other structures that enclose one or more seeds of an angiosperm.

fruiting body The reproductive hypha of a fungus.

fuel A material that releases energy when it burns.

fuel rod Uranium rod that undergoes fission in a nuclear reactor.

fulcrum The fixed point around which a lever pivots.

fullerene A form of the element carbon that consists of carbon atoms arranged in a repeating pattern similar to the surface of a soccer ball.

function The job or process that an organism's structure or part of its structure carries out.

fuse A safety device with a thin metal strip that will melt if too much current passes through a circuit.

galaxy A giant structure that contains hundreds of billions of stars.

gallbladder The organ that stores bile after it is produced by the liver.

galvanometer A device that uses the rotation of a loop of wire in a magnetic field to measure small amounts of current.

gamete A sperm cell or an egg cell.

gametophyte The stage in the life cycle of a plant in which the plant produces gametes, or sex cells.

gamma radiation A type of nuclear radiation made of high-energy waves.

gamma rays Electromagnetic waves with the shortest wavelengths and highest frequencies.

gas A state of matter with no definite shape or volume.

gas giant The name given to the first four outer planets: Jupiter, Saturn, Uranus, and Neptune.

gasohol A mixture of gasoline and alcohol.

gastropod A mollusk with a single shell or no shell.

Glossary

gears Two or more wheels linked together by interlocking teeth.

gemstone A hard, colorful mineral that has a brilliant or glassy luster.

gene A segment of DNA on a chromosome that codes for a specific trait.

gene therapy The insertion of working copies of a gene into the cells of a person with a genetic disorder in an attempt to correct the disorder.

genetic disorder An abnormal condition that a person inherits through genes or chromosomes.

genetic engineering The transfer of a gene from the DNA of one organism into another organism, in order to produce an organism with desired traits.

genetics The scientific study of heredity.

genome All of the DNA in one cell of an organism.

genotype An organism's genetic makeup, or allele combinations.

genus A classification grouping that consists of a number of similar, closely related species.

geocentric A description of the solar system in which all of the planets revolve around Earth.

geologic time scale A record of the geologic events and life forms in Earth's history.

geologist A scientist who studies the forces that make and shape planet Earth.

geology The study of the solid Earth.

geosynchronous orbit The orbit of a satellite that revolves around Earth at the same rate that Earth rotates.

geothermal energy Heat energy in Earth's interior from water or steam that has been heated by magma.

germination The early growth stage of the embryo plant in a seed.

gestation period The length of time between fertilization and birth of a mammal.

geyser A type of hot spring that builds up pressure underground and erupts at regular intervals as a fountain of water and steam.

giant star A very large star, much larger than the sun.

gill A breathing organ that removes oxygen from water.

gizzard A thick-walled, muscular part of a bird's stomach that squeezes and grinds partially digested food.

glacier A huge mass of ice and snow that moves slowly over the land.

glass A clear, solid material with no crystal structure, created by heating sand to a very high temperature.

Global Positioning System A method of finding latitude and longitude using satellites.

global warming A gradual increase in the temperature of Earth's atmosphere.

global winds Winds that blow steadily from specific directions over long distances.

globe A sphere that represents Earth's surface.

glucose A sugar that is the major source of energy for the body's cells; the monomer of many complex carbohydrates.

Golgi body A structure in a cell that receives proteins and other newly formed materials from the endoplasmic reticulum, packages them, and distributes them to other parts of the cell.

gradual metamorphosis A type of metamorphosis in which an egg hatches into a nymph that resembles an adult, and which has no distinctly different larval stage.

gradualism The theory that evolution occurs slowly but steadily.

grain A particle of mineral or other rock that gives a rock its texture.

gram A unit of measure for measuring mass, or the amount of matter in an object.

granite A usually light-colored rock that is found in continental crust.

graph A diagram that shows how two variables are related.

graphite A form of the element carbon in which carbon atoms form flat layers.

Skills and Content Review

grassland An area populated by grasses that gets 25 to 75 centimeters of rain each year.

gravitational potential energy Potential energy that depends on the height of an object.

gravity The attractive force between two objects; its magnitude depends on their masses and the distance between them.

greenhouse effect The process by which heat is trapped in the atmosphere by water vapor, carbon dioxide, methane, and other gases that form a "blanket" around earth.

greenhouse gases Gases in the atmosphere that trap heat.

groin A stone or concrete wall built out from a beach to reduce erosion.

grounded Term used to describe a circuit that allows charges to flow directly from the circuit to the ground connection.

groundwater Water that fills the cracks and spaces in underground soil and rock layers.

group Elements in the same vertical column of the periodic table; also called family.

gully A large channel in soil formed by erosion.

gymnosperm A plant that produces seeds that are not enclosed by a protective covering.

habitat The place where an organism lives and that provides the things it needs to survive.

habitat destruction The loss of a natural habitat.

habitat fragmentation The breaking of a habitat into smaller, isolated pieces.

half-life The time it takes for half of the atoms of a radioactive isotope sample to decay.

halogen family The elements in Group 17 of the periodic table.

hanging wall The block of rock that forms the upper half of a fault.

hard disk The rigid magnetic metal disk that stays inside a computer and holds information that can be accessed any time the computer is on.

hardness The level of the minerals calcium and magnesium in water.

hazardous waste A material that can be harmful if it is not properly disposed of.

headwaters The many small streams that come together at the source of the river.

heart A hollow, muscular organ that pumps blood throughout the body.

heart attack A condition in which blood flow to a part of the heart muscle is blocked, which causes heart cells to die.

heat Thermal energy that is transferred from a warmer object to a cooler one.

heat engine A device that converts thermal energy into mechanical energy.

heat transfer The movement of thermal energy from a warmer object to a cooler object.

heliocentric A description of the solar system in which all of the planets revolve around the sun.

hemisphere One half of the sphere that makes up Earth's surface.

hemoglobin An iron-containing protein that binds chemically to oxygen molecules and makes up most of a red blood cell.

herbivore An animal that eats only plants.

heredity The passing of traits from parents to offspring.

hertz (Hz) Unit of measurement for frequency.

Hertzsprung-Russell diagram A graph relating the temperature and brightness of stars.

heterotroph An organism that cannot make its own food.

heterozygous Having two different alleles for a trait.

hibernation A state of greatly reduced body activity that some mammals enter in the winter.

histamine A chemical that is responsible for the symptoms of an allergy.

holdfast A bundle of rootlike strands that attaches algae to the rocks.

hologram A three-dimensional photograph formed by the interference between two laser beams.

Glossary

homeostasis The process by which an organism's internal environment is kept stable in spite of changes in the external environment.

homologous structures Body parts that are structurally similar in related species; provide evidence that the structures were inherited from a common ancestor.

homozygous Having two identical alleles for a trait.

hormone (1) A chemical that affects a plant's growth and development. (2) The chemical product of an endocrine gland that speeds up or slows down the activities of an organ or tissue.

host An organism that provides a source of energy or a suitable environment for a virus or for another organism to live.

hot spot An area where magma from deep within the mantle melts through the crust above it.

hot spring A pool formed by groundwater that has risen to the surface after being heated by a nearby body of magma.

humid subtropical A wet and warm climate area on the edge of the tropics.

humidity A measure of the amount of water vapor in the air.

humus Dark-colored organic material in soil.

hurricane A tropical storm that has winds of 119 kilometers per hour or higher; typically about 600 kilometers across.

hybrid An organism that has two different alleles for a trait; an organism that is heterozygous for a particular trait.

hybridization A selective breeding method in which two genetically different individuals are crossed.

hydraulic system A system that multiplies force by transmitting pressure from a small surface area through a confined fluid to a larger surface area.

hydrocarbon An organic compound that contains only the elements carbon and hydrogen.

hydroelectric power Electricity produced by the kinetic energy of water moving over a waterfall or dam.

hydrogen ion A positively charged ion (H+) formed of a hydrogen atom that has lost its electron.

hydroponics The method of growing plants in a solution of nutrients instead of in soil.

hydrosphere Earth's water and ice. One of the four spheres into which scientists divide Earth.

hydrothermal vent An area where ocean water sinks through cracks in the ocean floor, is heated by the underlying magma, and rises again through the cracks.

hydroxide ion A negatively charged ion made of oxygen and hydrogen (OH−).

hydroxyl group A group of atoms, −OH group, found in alcohols.

hypertension A disorder in which a person's blood pressure is consistently higher than normal.

hypha One of many branching, threadlike tubes that make up the body of a fungus.

hypothalamus A tiny part of the brain that links the nervous system and the endocrine system.

hypothesis A possible explanation for a set of observations or an answer to a scientific question; must be testable.

ice age Cold time periods in Earth's history, during which glaciers covered large parts of the surface.

ice wedging Process that splits rock when water seeps into cracks, then freezes and expands.

ideal mechanical advantage The mechanical advantage that a machine would have without friction.

igneous rock A type of rock that forms from the cooling of molten rock at or below the surface.

illuminated Word used to describe an object that can be seen because it reflects light.

image A copy of an object formed by reflected or refracted rays of light.

immigration Moving into a population.

immune response Part of the body's defense against pathogens in which cells of the immune system react to each kind of pathogen with a defense targeted specifically at that pathogen.

Skills and Content Review

GLOSSARY

immunity The ability of the immune system to destroy pathogens before they can cause disease.

impermeable Characteristic of materials through which water does not easily pass, such as clay and granite.

imprinting A process in which newly hatched birds or newborn mammals learn to follow the first object they see.

inbreeding A selective breeding method in which two individuals with identical or similar sets of alleles are crossed.

incandescent lights Lights that glow when a filament inside them gets hot.

incineration The burning of solid waste.

incisors Flat-edged teeth used to bite off and cut parts of food.

inclined plane A simple machine consisting of a flat surface with one end higher than the other.

independent variable See manipulated variable.

index fossils Fossils of widely distributed organisms that lived during only one short period.

index of refraction The measure of how much a ray of light bends when it enters a new medium.

indicator A compound that changes color in contact with an acid or a base.

induction The movement of electrons to one part of an object caused by the electric field of another object.

inertia The tendency of a moving object to continue in a straight line or of a stationary object to remain in place.

inexhaustible resources Any living or nonliving thing in the environment of which there is a limitless supply.

infectious disease A disease that can pass from one organism to another.

inference A logical interpretation based on observation and prior knowledge.

inflammatory response Part of the body's defense against pathogens, in which fluid and white blood cells leak from blood vessels into tissues; the white blood cells destroy pathogens by breaking them down.

infrared radiation A form of energy with wavelengths that are longer than visible light.

infrared rays Electromagnetic waves with higher frequencies and shorter wavelengths than radio waves.

infrasound Sound waves with frequencies below 20 Hz.

inhibitor A material that decreases the rate of a reaction.

inner core A dense sphere of solid iron and nickel in the center of Earth.

inorganic Not formed from living things or the remains of living things.

inorganic compound A compound that does not contain carbon.

input device A device, such as a keyboard, that feeds data to a computer.

input force The force exerted on a machine.

insect An arthropod with three body sections, six legs, one pair of antennae, and usually one or two pairs of wings.

insight learning The process of learning how to solve a problem or do something new by applying what is already known.

instinct An inborn behavior pattern that an animal performs correctly the first time.

insulation Building material that blocks heat transfer between the air inside and outside.

insulator A material that does not easily transfer thermal energy or electric current between its particles.

insulin A chemical produced in the pancreas that enables the body's cells to take in glucose from the blood and use it for energy.

integrated circuit An electrical circuit manufactured on a tiny slice of semiconductor or chip.

intellectual property A story, poem, computer program, or similar product whose ownership is legally protected.

intensity The amount of energy per second carried through a unit area by a wave.

interference The interaction between waves that meet.

GLOSSARY

Glossary

internal combustion engine An engine that burns fuel inside cylinders within the engine.

internal stimulus A change from within an organism, such as hunger and thirst, that causes the organism to respond.

International System of Units (SI) A system of measurement based on multiples of ten and on established measures of mass, length, and time; used by scientists to measure the properties of matter.

Internet A global computer network that links millions of computers in businesses, schools, and research organizations.

interneuron A neuron that carries nerve impulses from one neuron to another.

interphase The stage of the cell cycle that takes place before cell division occurs; during this stage, the cell grows, copies its DNA, and prepares to divide.

intertidal zone The area on a seashore between the highest high-tide line and the lowest low-tide line.

intrusion An igneous rock layer formed when magma hardens beneath Earth's surface.

intrusive rock Igneous rock that forms when magma hardens beneath Earth's surface.

invertebrate An animal that does not have a backbone.

involuntary muscle A muscle that is not under conscious control.

ion An atom or group of atoms that is electrically charged.

ionic bond The attraction between two oppositely charged ions.

ionosphere The lower part of the thermosphere, where electrically charged particles called ions are found.

iris The ring of colored muscle that surrounds the pupil and regulates the amount of light entering the eye.

irregular galaxy A galaxy that does not have a regular shape.

irrigation The process of supplying water to areas of land to make them suitable for growing crops.

island arc A string of islands formed by the volcanoes along a deep ocean trench.

isobars Lines on a map joining places that have the same air pressure.

isomer One of a number of compounds that have the same molecular formula but different structures.

isotherms Lines on a map joining places that have the same temperature.

isotope An atom with the same number of protons and different number of neutrons from other atoms of the same element.

jet streams Bands of high-speed winds about 10 kilometers above Earth's surface.

joint A place where two bones come together.

joule A unit of work equal to one newton-meter.

karst topography A type of landscape in rainy regions where there is limestone near the surface, characterized by caverns, sinkholes, and valleys.

karyotype A picture of all the chromosomes in a cell arranged in pairs.

Kelvin scale The temperature scale on which zero is the temperature at which no more energy can be removed from matter.

kettle A small depression that forms when a chunk of ice is left in glacial till.

key A list of the symbols used on a map.

keystone species A species that influences the survival of many others in an ecosystem.

kidney A major organ of the excretory system; removes urea, excess water, and other waste materials from the body.

kinetic energy Energy that an object has due to its motion.

labor The first stage of birth, in which strong muscular contractions of the uterus occur.

land breeze The flow of air from land to a body of water.

GLOSSARY

land reclamation The process of restoring land to a more natural state.

landform A feature of topography formed by the processes that shape Earth's surface.

landform region A large area of land where the topography is similar.

lanthanides A group of elements in the first row of the rare earth elements in the periodic table.

large intestine The last section of the digestive system, where water is absorbed from food and the remaining material is eliminated from the body.

larva The immature form of an animal that looks very different from the adult.

larynx Two folds of tissue that make up the human voice box; located in the top part of the trachea, underneath the epiglottis.

laser A device that produces coherent light.

latitude The distance north or south from the equator, measured in degrees.

lava Magma that reaches the surface; also the rock formed when liquid lava hardens.

lava flow The area covered by lava as it pours out of a volcano's vent.

law of conservation of energy The rule that energy cannot be created or destroyed.

law of conservation of momentum The rule that the total momentum of objects in an interaction does not change.

law of superposition The geologic principle that states that in horizontal layers of sedimentary rock, each layer is older than the layer above it and younger than the layer below it.

leach field The ground area around a septic tank through which wastewater filters after leaving the tank.

leachate Water that has passed through buried wastes in a landfill.

leaf The organ of a vascular plant where photosynthesis occurs.

learning The process that leads to changes in behavior based on practice or experience.

leeward The downwind side of mountains.

lens (1) A curved piece of glass or other transparent material that is used to refract light. (2) The flexible structure that focuses light that has entered the eye.

levee A long ridge formed by deposits of sediments alongside a river channel.

lever A simple machine consisting of a rigid object that pivots about a fixed point.

lichen The combination of a fungus and either an alga or an autotrophic bacterium that live together in a mutualistic relationship.

lift An upward force on an object that results from the difference in pressure between the upper and lower surfaces of the object.

ligament Strong connective tissue that holds together the bones in a movable joint.

light-year The distance that light travels in one year.

lightning A sudden spark, or energy discharge, caused when electrical charges jump between parts of a cloud or between a cloud and the ground.

lightning rod A metal rod on a building connected to a grounding wire; meant to protect a building from lightning damage.

limiting factor An environmental factor that prevents a population from increasing.

linear Term used to describe a relationship between variables whose graph is a straight line.

lipids Energy-rich organic compounds, such as fats, oils, and waxes, made of carbon, hydrogen, and oxygen.

liquefaction The process by which an earthquake's violent movement suddenly turns loose soil into liquid mud.

liquid A state of matter that has no definite shape but has a definite volume.

lithosphere A rigid layer made up of the uppermost part of the mantle and the crust. One of four spheres into which scientists divide Earth.

litter The loose layer of dead plant leaves and stems on the surface of the soil.

liver The largest and heaviest organ in the body; it breaks down substances and eliminates nitrogen from the body.

load The amount of sediment that a river or stream carries.

loam Rich, fertile soil that is made up of about equal parts of clay, sand, and silt.

local area network (LAN) A set of computers connected in one office building or classroom.

local winds Winds that blow over short distances.

loess A wind-formed deposit made of fine particles of clay and silt.

longitude The distance in degrees east or west of the prime meridian.

longitudinal wave A wave that moves the medium parallel to the direction in which the wave travels.

longshore drift The movement of water and sediment along a beach caused by waves coming into shore at an angle.

loudness Perception of the intensity of a sound.

luminous Word used to describe an object that can be seen because it emits light.

lunar eclipse The blocking of sunlight to the moon that occurs when Earth is directly between the sun and moon.

lungs The main organs of the respiratory system, where gas exchange takes place.

luster The way a mineral reflects light from its surface.

lymph The fluid that the lymphatic system collects and returns to the bloodstream.

lymph node A small knob of tissue in the lymphatic system that filters lymph.

lymphatic system A network of veinlike vessels that returns the fluid that leaks out of blood vessels to the bloodstream.

lymphocyte White blood cell that reacts to each kind of pathogen with a defense targeted specifically at that pathogen.

lysosome A small round cell structure that contains chemicals that break down large food particles into smaller ones.

machine A device that changes the amount of force exerted or the direction in which force is exerted.

magma The molten mixture of rock-forming substances, gases, and water that makes up part of Earth's mantle.

magma chamber The pocket beneath a volcano where magma collects.

magnetic A characteristic of those metals that are attracted to magnets and can be made into magnets.

magnetic declination The angle between geographic north and the north to which a compass needle points.

magnetic domain A region in which the magnetic fields of all atoms line up in one direction.

magnetic field The region around a magnet where the magnetic force is exerted.

magnetic field lines Lines that map out the magnetic field around a magnet.

magnetic pole The ends of a magnetic object, where the magnetic force is strongest.

magnetic resonance imaging (MRI) A process that uses radio waves to form pictures of the inside of the human body.

magnetism The force of attraction or repulsion of magnetic materials.

magnetosphere The region of Earth's magnetic field confined by the solar wind.

magnification The ability to make things look larger than they are.

magnitude The measurement of an earthquake's strength based on seismic waves and movement along faults.

main sequence An area on the Hertzsprung-Russell diagram that runs from the upper left to the lower right and includes more than 90 percent of all stars.

Glossary

malleable A term used to describe material that can be pounded or rolled into shape.

mammal A warm-blooded vertebrate with a four-chambered heart, skin covered with fur or hair, and has young fed with milk from the mother's body.

mammary glands The organs that produce the milk with which mammals feed their young.

manipulated variable The one factor that a scientist changes to test a hypothesis during an experiment; also called independent variable.

mantle The layer of hot, solid material between Earth's crust and core.

map A model of all or part of Earth's surface as seen from above.

map projection A framework of lines that helps to show landmasses correctly on a flat surface.

maria Dark, flat regions on the moon's surface.

marine climate The climate of some coastal regions, with relatively warm winters and cool summers.

maritime (air mass) A humid air mass that forms over oceans.

marrow The soft tissue that fills the internal spaces in bone.

marsupial A mammal whose young are born alive at an early stage of development and continue to develop in a pouch on their mother's body.

mass A measure of how much matter is in an object.

mass extinction When many types of living things become extinct at the same time.

mass movement Any one of several processes by which gravity moves sediment downhill.

mass number The sum of the protons and neutrons in the nucleus of an atom.

matter Anything that has mass and occupies space.

meander A looping curve formed in a river as it winds through its flood plain.

mechanical advantage The number of times the force exerted on a machine is multiplied.

mechanical digestion The physical process that tears, grinds, and mashes large food particles into smaller ones.

mechanical energy Kinetic or potential energy associated with the motion or position of an object.

mechanical wave A wave that requires a medium through which to travel.

mechanical weathering The type of weathering in which rock is physically broken into smaller pieces.

medium Material through which a wave travels.

medusa The cnidarian body plan characterized by a bowl shape and which is adapted for a free-swimming life.

meiosis The process that occurs in sex cells (sperm and egg) by which the number of chromosomes is reduced by half.

melanin A pigment that gives the skin its color.

meltdown A dangerous condition caused by overheating inside a nuclear reactor.

melting The change from the solid to the liquid form, or state, of matter.

melting point The temperature at which a substance changes from a solid into a liquid.

menstrual cycle The monthly cycle of changes that occurs in the female reproductive system, during which an egg develops and the uterus prepares for the arrival of a fertilized egg.

menstruation The process that occurs if fertilization does not take place, in which the thickened lining of the uterus breaks down and blood and tissue then pass out of the female body through the vagina.

mental health A component of wellness that involves a person's feelings, or emotions.

Mercalli scale A scale that rates earthquakes according to their intensity and how much damage they cause.

mercury barometer An instrument that measures changes in air pressure, consisting of a glass tube partially filled with mercury, with its open end resting in a dish of mercury. Air pressure pushing on the mercury in the dish forces the mercury in the tube higher.

mesosphere The middle layer of Earth's atmosphere; the layer in which most meteoroids burn up.

messenger RNA RNA that copies the coded message from DNA in the nucleus and carries the message into the cytoplasm.

metalloid An element that has some of the characteristics of metals and some of the characteristics of nonmetals.

metamorphic rock A type of rock that forms from an existing rock that is changed by heat, pressure, or chemical reactions.

metamorphosis A process in which an animal's body undergoes dramatic changes in form during its life cycle.

meteor A streak of light in the sky produced by the burning of a meteoroid in Earth's atmosphere.

meteorite A meteoroid that has hit Earth's surface.

meteoroid A chunk of rock or dust in space.

meteorologists Scientists who study the causes of weather and try to predict it.

meter The basic SI unit of length.

microclimate The climate of a small, specific area; it may be different from the climate of the surrounding area.

microscope An optical instrument that forms enlarged images of tiny objects.

microwaves Radio waves with the shortest wavelengths and the highest frequencies.

mid-ocean ridge The undersea mountain chain where new ocean floor is produced; a divergent plate boundary.

middle ear The space behind the eardrum.

migration The regular, periodic journey of an animal from one place to another and back again for the purpose of feeding or reproduction.

mineral (1) A naturally occurring inorganic solid that has a crystal structure and a definite chemical composition. (2) A nutrient that is needed by the body in small amounts and is not made by living things.

mirage An image of a distant object caused by refraction of light as it travels through air of varying temperature.

mitochondria Rod-shaped cell structures that produce most of the energy needed to carry out the cell's functions.

mitosis The stage of the cell cycle during which the cell's nucleus divides into two new nuclei, and one copy of the DNA is distributed into each daughter cell.

mixture Two or more substances that are mixed together but are not chemically combined.

Mohs hardness scale A scale ranking ten minerals from softest to hardest; used in testing the hardness of minerals.

molars Teeth that, along with premolars, grind and shred food into tiny bits.

mold A type of fossil formed when an organism buried in sediment dissolves, leaving a hollow area.

molecular compound A compound consisting of molecules of covalently bonded atoms.

molecular formula A combination of chemical symbols that represent the elements in each molecule of a compound.

molecule A combination of two or more atoms that are bonded together; the smallest unit of most compounds.

mollusk An invertebrate with a soft, unsegmented body; most of them are protected by hard outer shells.

molting The process of shedding an outgrown exoskeleton.

moment magnitude scale A scale that rates earthquakes by estimating the total energy released by an earthquake.

momentum The product of an object's mass and velocity.

monocot An angiosperm that has only one seed leaf.

monomer Small, carbon-based molecules that make up the links in a polymer chain.

GLOSSARY

monotreme A mammal that lays eggs.

monsoons Sea and land breezes over a large region that change direction with the seasons.

moraine A ridge formed by the till deposited at the edge of a glacier.

motion The state in which one object's distance from another is changing.

motor neuron A neuron that sends an impulse to a muscle, causing the muscle to contract.

mountain A landform with high elevation and high relief.

mountain range A series of mountains that have the same general shape and structure.

mouth The point where a river flows into another body of water.

mucus A thick, slippery substance produced by the body.

multicellular A type of organism that is made up of many cells.

multiple alleles Three or more forms of a gene that code for a single trait.

municipal solid waste Waste produced in homes, businesses, and schools.

muscle tissue A body tissue that contracts or shortens, making body parts move.

music A set of tones and overtones combined in ways that are pleasing to the ear.

mutation A change in a gene or chromosome.

mutualism A type of symbiosis in which both partners benefit from living together.

native species Species that have naturally evolved in an area.

natural hazard An event that results from Earth processes and that can cause damage and endanger human life.

natural selection The process by which individuals that are better adapted to their environment are more likely to survive and reproduce than other members of the same species.

neap tide A tide with the least difference between low and high tide that occurs when the sun and moon pull at right angles to each other.

nearsightedness The condition in which nearby objects can be seen clearly but distant objects look blurry.

nebula A large amount of gas and dust in space, spread out in an immense volume.

negative feedback A process in which a system is turned off by the condition it produces; examples of negative feedback systems include regulation of temperature by a thermostat and the regulation of the levels of many hormones in the blood.

nekton Free-swimming animals that can move throughout the water column.

neon lights Glass tubes filled with neon that produce light.

nephron One of a million tiny, filtering structures found in the kidneys that removes wastes from blood and produces urine.

neritic zone The region of shallow ocean water that extends from the low-tide line out to the edge of the continental shelf.

nerve A bundle of nerve fibers.

nerve impulse The message carried by a neuron.

nerve tissue A body tissue that carries messages back and forth between the brain and every other part of the body.

net force The overall force on an object when all the individual forces acting on an object are added together.

neuron A cell that carries messages through the nervous system.

neutralization A reaction between an acid and a base.

neutron A small particle in the nucleus of the atom, with no electrical charge.

neutron star A tiny star that remains after a supernova explosion.

newton A unit of measure that equals the force required to accelerate one kilogram of mass at 1 meter per second per second.

Glossary

niche An organism's particular role in an ecosystem, or how it makes its living.

nicotine A drug in tobacco that speeds up the activities of the nervous system, heart, and other organs of the body.

nitrogen fixation The process of changing free nitrogen gas into a usable form.

noble gas An element in Group 18 of the periodic table.

node A point of zero amplitude on a standing wave.

nodule (1) A black, potato-shaped lump formed when metals build up around pieces of shell on the ocean floor. (2) A bump on the roots of certain plants that houses nitrogen-fixing bacteria.

noise A mixture of sound waves with no pleasing timbre and no identifiable pitch.

noninfectious disease A disease that is not spread from person to person.

nonlinear Term used to describe a relationship between variables whose graph is not a straight line.

nonmetal An element that lacks most of the properties of metals.

nonpoint source A widely spread source of pollution that is difficult to link to a specific point of origin, such as road runoff.

nonpolar The description of a covalent bond in which electrons are shared equally, or of a molecule containing nonpolar bonds or polar bonds that cancel out.

nonrenewable resource A natural resource that is not replaced as it is used.

nonvascular plant A low-growing plant that lacks vascular tissue.

normal fault A type of fault where the hanging wall slides downward; caused by tension in the crust.

notochord A flexible rod that supports a chordate's back.

nuclear energy The potential energy stored in the nucleus of an atom.

nuclear fission The splitting of an atom's nucleus into smaller nuclei.

nuclear fusion The process in which smaller nuclei combine into larger nuclei, forming heavier elements and releasing energy.

nuclear radiation Particles and energy produced during radioactive decay.

nuclear reaction A reaction involving the particles in the nucleus of an atom that can change one element into another element.

nucleic acid A very large organic compound made up of carbon, oxygen, hydrogen, nitrogen, and phosphorus; examples are DNA and RNA; contains instructions that cells need to carry out all the functions of life.

nucleotide One of several organic molecules that are the monomers of nucleic acids.

nucleus (1) The control center of a cell that directs the cell's activities; contains the chemical instructions that direct all the cell's activities and determine the cell's characteristics. (2) The central core of an atom, containing protons and usually neutrons.

nutrient A substance that provides energy or raw materials for the body to grow, repair worn parts, or function properly.

nutrient depletion The situation that arises when more soil nutrients are used than the decomposers can replace.

nymph A stage of gradual metamorphosis that usually resembles the adult insect.

objective lens Lens that gathers light from an object and forms a real image.

observation Using one or more of the five senses to gather information.

observatory A building that contains one or more telescopes.

occluded Cut off, as the warm air mass at an occluded front is cut off from the ground by cooler air beneath it.

Skills and Content Review

GLOSSARY

oceanographer A scientist who studies Earth's oceans.

Ohm's law The rule that resistance equals voltage divided by current.

omnivore An animal that eats both plants and animals.

opaque A material that reflects or absorbs all light that strikes it.

open-ocean zone The area of the ocean beyond the edge of the continental shelf.

operational definition A statement that describes how a particular variable is to be measured or a term is to be defined.

optic nerve Short, thick nerve that carries signals from the eye to the brain.

optical disc A disc on which information is written and read by lasers.

optical fiber A long, thin strand of glass or plastic that can carry light for long distances without allowing the light to fade out; can be used for transmitting messages.

orbit The path of an object as it revolves around another object in space.

ore Rock that contains a metal or economically useful mineral.

organ A structure in the body that is composed of different kinds of tissue.

organ system A group of organs that work together to perform a major function in the body.

organelle A tiny cell structure that carries out a specific function within the cell.

organic acid A substituted hydrocarbon with one or more of the $-COOH$ group of atoms.

organic compound Most compounds that contain carbon.

organic rock Sedimentary rock that forms where remains of organisms are deposited in thick layers.

organism A living thing.

osmosis The diffusion of water molecules through a selectively permeable membrane.

osteoporosis A condition in which the body's bones become weak and break easily.

outer core A layer of molten iron and nickel that surrounds the inner core of Earth.

output device A device that presents data from a computer; a monitor is an output device.

output force The force exerted on an object by a machine.

ovary (1) A protective structure in plants that encloses the developing seeds. (2) Organ of the female reproductive system in which eggs and estrogen are produced.

oviduct A passageway for eggs from an ovary to the uterus; the place where fertilization usually occurs.

ovulation The process in which a mature egg is released from the ovary into an oviduct; occurs about halfway through a typical menstrual cycle.

ovule A plant structure in seed plants that contains an egg cell.

oxbow lake The crescent-shaped, cut-off body of water that remains after a river carves a new channel.

ozone A form of oxygen that has three oxygen atoms in each molecule instead of the usual two; can be toxic.

ozone layer The layer of the atmosphere that contains a higher concentration of ozone than the rest of the atmosphere.

P wave A type of seismic wave that compresses and expands the ground.

pacemaker A group of cells located in the right atrium that sends out signals that make the heart muscle contract and that regulates heartbeat rate.

pahoehoe A hot, fast-moving type of lava that hardens to form smooth, ropelike coils.

paleontologist A scientist who studies extinct organisms, examines fossil structure, and makes comparisons to present-day organisms in order to learn about organisms that lived long ago.

© Pearson Education, Inc.

pancreas A triangular organ that produces enzymes that flow into the small intestine.

Pangaea The name of the single landmass that broke apart 200 million years ago and gave rise to today's continents.

parallax The apparent change in position of an object when seen from different places.

parallel circuit An electric circuit with several paths for the current to take.

parasite An organism that lives on or in a host and causes harm to the host.

parasitism A relationship in which one organism lives on or inside another and harms it.

pascal A unit of pressure equal to one newton per square meter.

Pascal's principle The rule that when force is applied to a confined fluid, the increase in pressure is transmitted equally to all parts of the fluid.

passive immunity Immunity in which the antibodies that fight a pathogen come from another organism rather than from the person's own body.

passive smoking The involuntary inhalation of smoke from other people's cigarettes, cigars, or pipes.

passive solar system A method of converting solar energy into heat without pumps or fans.

passive transport The movement of materials through a cell membrane without using energy.

pasteurization A heating process that is widely used to kill microorganisms in food products such as milk.

pathogen An organism that causes disease.

peat The blackish-brown material consisting of compressed layers of dead sphagnum mosses that grow in bogs.

pedigree A chart or "family tree" that tracks which members of a family have a particular trait.

peer pressure The pressure from friends and classmates to behave in certain ways.

penis The organ through which both semen and urine leave the male body.

penumbra The part of a shadow surrounding the darkest part.

Percent Daily Value An indication of how the nutritional content of a food fits into the diet of a person who consumes a total of 2,000 Calories a day.

period (1) A horizontal row of elements in the periodic table. (2) One of the units of geologic time into which geologists divide eras.

periodic table An arrangement of the elements in order of atomic number, in which elements with similar properties are grouped in columns.

peripheral nervous system All the nerves located outside the central nervous system; connects the central nervous system to all parts of the body.

peristalsis Involuntary waves of muscle contraction that keep food moving along in one direction through the digestive system.

permafrost Soil that is frozen all year; found in the tundra climate region.

permanent magnet A magnet made of material that keeps its magnetism.

permeable Characteristic of materials such as sand and gravel which allow water to pass easily through them.

pesticide A chemical intended to kill insects and other organisms that damage crops.

petal The colorful, leaflike structures of a flower.

petrified fossil A fossil formed when minerals replace all or part of an organism.

petrochemical Compound made from oil.

petroleum Liquid fossil fuel; oil.

pH How acidic or basic a substance is, measured on a scale of 0 (very acidic) to 14 (very basic).

pH scale A range of values from 0 to 14 that expresses the concentration of hydrogen ions in a solution.

phagocyte A white blood cell that destroys pathogens by engulfing them and breaking them down.

pharynx The throat; part of both the respiratory and digestive systems.

phase One of the different shapes of the moon as seen from Earth.

phenotype An organism's physical appearance, or visible traits.

pheromone A chemical released by one animal that affects the behavior of another animal of the same species.

phloem The vascular tissue through which food moves in some plants.

photochemical smog A brownish haze that is a mixture of ozone and other chemicals, formed when nitrogen oxides, hydrocarbons, and other pollutants react with one another in the presence of sunlight.

photoelectric effect The movement of electrons in a substance when light is shined on it.

photon A tiny particle or packet of light energy.

photosphere The inner layer of the sun's atmosphere.

photosynthesis The process by which plants and some other organisms capture light energy and use it to make food from carbon dioxide and water.

physical change A change that alters the form or appearance of a substance but does not make the material into another substance.

physical health A component of wellness that consists of how well the body functions.

physical property A characteristic of a substance that can be observed without changing the substance into something else.

physical science The study of matter, energy, and the changes that matter and energy undergo.

pigment A colored chemical compound that absorbs light; pigments are opaque and are used to color other materials.

pioneer species The first species to populate an area.

pipe A long tube through which magma moves from the magma chamber to Earth's surface.

pistil The female reproductive parts of a flower.

pitch Perception of the frequency of a sound.

pituitary gland An endocrine gland just below the hypothalamus that communicates with the hypothalamus to control many body activities.

pixels The tiny dots in a satellite image or other computer-generated image.

placenta A membrane that becomes the link between the developing embryo or fetus and the mother.

placental mammal A mammal that develops inside its mother's body until its body systems can function independently.

plain A landform made up of flat or gently rolling land with low relief.

plane mirror A flat mirror that produces an upright, virtual image the same size as the object.

plankton Tiny algae and animals that float in water and are carried by waves and currents.

plasma (1) A state of matter in which atoms are stripped of their electrons and the nuclei are packed closely together. (2) The liquid part of blood.

plastic A synthetic polymer that can be molded or shaped.

plate A section of the lithosphere that slowly moves over the asthenosphere, carrying pieces of continental and oceanic crust.

plate boundary A crack in the lithosphere where two of Earth's plates meet.

plate tectonics The theory that pieces of Earth's lithosphere are in constant motion, driven by convection currents in the mantle.

plateau A landform that has a more or less level surface and is elevated high above sea level.

platelet A cell fragment that plays an important part in forming blood clots.

plucking The process by which a glacier picks up rocks as it flows over the land.

poaching The illegal killing or removal of wildlife.

point source A specific source of pollution that can be identified, such as a pipe.

polar The description of a covalent bond in which electrons are shared unequally, or of a molecule containing polar bonds that do not cancel out.

GLOSSARY

Glossary

polar (air mass) A cold air mass that forms north of 50° north latitude or south of 50° south latitude and has high air pressure.

polar molecule A molecule that has electrically charged areas.

polar zones The areas near both poles, from about 66.5° to 90° north and 66.5° to 90° south latitudes.

polarized light Light that vibrates in only one direction.

pollen Tiny particles produced by plants that contain the microscopic cells that later become sperm cells.

pollination The transfer of pollen from male reproductive structures to female reproductive structures in plants.

pollutants Harmful substances in the air, water, or soil.

pollution A change to the environment that has a negative effect on living things.

polyatomic ion An ion that is made of more than one atom.

polymer A large, complex molecule built from smaller molecules bonded together.

polyp The cnidarian body plan characterized by a vaselike shape and which is usually adapted for life attached to an underwater surface.

population All the members of one species in a particular area.

population density The number of individuals in a specific area.

pore (1) An opening through which sweat reaches the surface of the skin. (2) a tiny opening in and between particles of rock and soil; may contain air or water.

porphyritic texture An igneous rock texture in which large crystals are scattered on a background of much smaller crystals.

potential difference The difference in electrical potential between two places; measured in volts.

potential energy Energy that is stored and available to be used later.

power The rate at which work is done or the rate at which one form of energy is converted into another.

precipitate A solid that forms from a solution during a chemical reaction.

precipitation Forms of water such as rain, snow, sleet, and hail, that fall from clouds and reach Earth's surface.

predation An interaction in which one organism hunts and kills another animal for food.

predator A carnivore that hunts and kills other animals for food and has adaptations that help it capture the animals it preys upon.

predicting Making an inference about a future event based on current evidence or past experience.

premolars Teeth that, along with molars, grind and shred food into tiny bits.

preservation viewpoint The belief that all parts of the environment are equally important, no matter how useful they are to humans.

pressure The force exerted on a surface divided by the total area over which the force is exerted; also the force of a gas's outward push divided by the area of the walls of the container.

prey An animal that a predator feeds upon.

primary colors Three colors that can be used to make any other color.

primary succession The changes that occur in an area where no ecosystem had existed.

primary treatment The removal of solid materials from wastewater.

primary wave A longitudinal seismic wave.

prime meridian The line that makes a half circle from the North Pole to the South Pole and that passes through Greenwich, England.

probability The likelihood that a particular event will occur.

producer An organism that can make its own food.

product A substance formed as a result of a chemical reaction.

GLOSSARY

Skills and Content Review

projectile An object that is thrown.

prokaryote An organism whose cells lack a nucleus and some other cell structures.

prominence A loop of gas that protrudes from the sun's surface, linking sunspots.

protein Large organic molecule made of carbon, hydrogen, oxygen, nitrogen, and sometimes sulfur; polymer of amino acids; they are needed for tissue growth and repair and play a part in chemical reactions within cells.

proton A small, positively charged particle in the nucleus of the atom.

protostar A contracting cloud of gas and dust; the earliest stage of a star's life.

protozoan An animal-like protist.

pseudopod A "false foot" or temporary bulge of the cell membrane used for feeding and movement in some protozoans.

psychrometer An instrument used to measure relative humidity, consisting of a wet-bulb thermometer and a dry-bulb thermometer.

puberty The period of sexual development during the teenage years in which the body becomes able to reproduce.

pulley A simple machine consisting of a grooved wheel around which is wrapped a rope, chain, or cable.

pulsar A neutron star that produces radio waves.

punctuated equilibria The theory that species evolve during short periods of rapid change.

Punnett square A chart that shows all the possible combinations of alleles that can result from a genetic cross.

pupa The second stage of complete metamorphosis, in which an insect is enclosed in a protective covering and gradually changes from a larva to an adult.

pupil The opening through which light enters the eye.

pure substance A substance made of only one kind of matter and having definite properties.

purebred An organism that always produces offspring with the same form of a trait as the parent.

pyroclastic flow The expulsion of ash, cinders, bombs, and gases during an explosive volcanic eruption.

quasar A distant galaxy with a black hole at its center.

radar A system of detecting reflected radio waves.

radial symmetry The quality of having many lines of symmetry that all pass through a central point.

radiation The direct transfer of energy through empty space by electromagnetic waves.

radiation therapy A process in which radioactive elements are used to destroy unhealthy cells.

radio telescope A device used to detect radio waves from objects in space.

radio waves Electromagnetic waves with the longest wavelengths and lowest frequencies.

radioactive Containing unstable atoms.

radioactive dating The process of determining the age of an object using the half-life of one or more radioactive isotopes.

radioactive decay The breakdown of the nucleus of a radioactive element, releasing particles and energy.

radioactive element An unstable particle that breaks down into a different element.

radula A flexible ribbon of tiny teeth in mollusks.

rain forest A forest in the tropical wet climate zone that gets plenty of rain all year.

rain gauge An instrument used to measure the amount of precipitation, consisting of an open-ended can topped by a collecting funnel and having a collecting tube and measuring scale inside.

Glossary

random-access memory (RAM) Temporary storage area for data while the computer is operating.

rarefaction The part of a longitudinal wave where the particles of the medium are far apart.

ray Straight line used to represent a light wave.

reactant A substance that enters into a chemical reaction.

reactivity The ease and speed with which an element or compound combines with other elements and compounds.

reactor vessel The part of a nuclear reactor where nuclear fission occurs.

read-only memory (ROM) The permanent storage area for data in the computer.

real image An inverted image formed where rays of light meet.

recessive allele An allele that is masked when a dominant allele is present.

recharge New water that enters an aquifer from the surface.

rechargeable battery A battery in which the products of the electrochemical reaction can be turned back into reactants to be reused.

rectum A short tube at the end of the large intestine where waste material is compressed into a solid form before being eliminated.

recycling The process of reclaiming and reusing raw materials.

red blood cell A cell in the blood that takes up oxygen in the lungs and delivers it to cells elsewhere in the body.

red tide An algal bloom that occurs in salt water.

reference point A place or object used for comparison to determine if an object is in motion.

refinery A factory where crude oil is separated into fuels and other products.

reflecting telescope A telescope that uses one or more mirrors to gather light from distant objects.

reflection The bouncing back of a wave when it hits a surface through which it cannot pass.

reflex An automatic response that occurs very rapidly and without conscious control.

refracting telescope A telescope that uses convex lenses to gather and focus light.

refraction The bending of waves as they enter a different medium.

regeneration The ability of an organism to regrow body parts.

regular reflection Reflection that occurs when parallel rays of light hit a smooth surface and all reflect at the same angle.

relative age The age of a rock compared to the ages of other rock layers.

relative dating A technique used to determine which of two fossils is older.

relative humidity The percentage of water vapor in the air compared to the maximum amount the air could hold at that temperature.

relief The difference in elevation between the highest and lowest parts of an area.

renewable resource A natural resource that can be replaced in nature at a rate close to the rate at which it is being used.

replacement reaction A reaction in which one element replaces another in a compound; or when two elements in different compounds trade places.

replication The process by which a cell makes a copy of the DNA in its nucleus.

reproduce The production of offspring that are similar to the parents.

reproduction The process by which living things produce new individuals of the same type.

reptile A vertebrate with scaly skin that lays eggs with tough, leathery shells; reptiles are ectothermic and have lungs.

reserve A known deposit of fuels.

reservoir A natural or artificial lake that stores water for human use.

Glossary

resin Solid material produced during oil refining that can be used to make plastics.

resistance The opposition to the movement of electric charges flowing through a material.

resistor A device in an electric circuit that uses electrical energy as it interferes with the flow of electric charge.

resolution The ability to clearly distinguish the individual parts of an object.

resonance The increase in the amplitude of vibration that occurs when external vibrations match the object's natural frequency.

respiration The process by which cells break down simple food molecules to release the energy they contain.

responding variable The factor that changes as a result of a change to the manipulated or independent variable in an experiment; also called dependent variable.

response An organism's action or change in behavior that occurs as a result of a stimulus.

retina The layer of receptor cells at the back of the eye on which an image is focused; nerve impulses are sent from the retina to the brain.

retrograde rotation The spinning motion of a planet from east to west, opposite to the direction of rotation of most planets and moons.

reverse fault A type of fault where the hanging wall slides upward; caused by compression in the crust.

revolution The movement of an object around another object.

rhizoid The thin, rootlike structure that anchors a moss and absorbs water and nutrients for the plant.

ribosome A small, grainlike structure in the cytoplasm of a cell where proteins are made.

Richter scale A scale that rates seismic waves as measured by a particular type of mechanical seismograph.

rift valley A deep valley that forms where two plates move apart.

rill A tiny groove in soil made by flowing water.

Ring of Fire A major belt of volcanoes that rims the Pacific Ocean.

rip current A rush of water that flows rapidly back to sea through a narrow opening.

river A large stream.

RNA Ribonucleic acid; a nucleic acid that plays an important role in the production of proteins; determines the order of amino acids in a protein.

rock The material that forms Earth's hard surface.

rock cycle A series of processes on the surface and inside Earth that slowly change rocks from one kind to another.

rods Cells on the retina that detect dim light.

rolling friction Friction that occurs when an object rolls over a surface.

root The underground part of any plant which anchors the plant in the ground and absorbs water and nutrients from the soil.

root cap A structure that covers the tip of a root, protecting the root from injury.

rotation The spinning motion of a planet about its axis.

runoff Water that flows over the ground surface rather than soaking into the ground.

S wave A type of seismic wave that moves the ground up and down or side to side.

salinity The total amount of dissolved salts in a water sample.

saliva The fluid released when the mouth waters that plays an important role in both mechanical and chemical digestion.

salt An ionic compound that can form from the neutralization of an acid with a base.

sand dune A deposit of wind-blown sand.

sandbar A ridge of sand deposited by waves as they slow down near shore.

sanitary landfill A landfill that holds nonhazardous waste such as municipal solid waste and construction debris.

GLOSSARY

Glossary

satellite Any object that revolves around another object in space.

satellite images Pictures of the land surface based on computer data collected from satellites.

saturated fats Fats, such as butter, that are usually solid at room temperature.

saturated hydrocarbons A hydrocarbon in which all the bonds between carbon atoms are single bonds.

saturated solution A mixture that has as much solute in it as possible at a given temperature.

saturated zone A layer of permeable rock or soil in which the cracks and pores are totally filled with water.

savanna A tropical grassland with scattered clumps of trees; found in the tropical wet-and-dry climate zone close to the equator.

scale Used to compare distance on a map or globe to distance on Earth's surface.

scattering Reflection of light in all directions.

scavenger A carnivore that feeds on the bodies of dead organisms.

science A way of learning about the natural world through observations and logical reasoning; leads to a body of knowledge.

scientific inquiry The diverse ways in which scientists study the natural world; another term for the ongoing process of discovery in science.

scientific law A statement that describes what scientists expect to happen every time under a particular set of conditions.

scientific theory A well-tested idea that explains and connects a wide range of observations.

screw A simple machine that consists of an inclined plane wrapped around a central cylinder to form a spiral.

scrotum An external pouch of skin in which the testes are located.

scrubber A device that uses water droplets to clean smokestack emissions.

sea breeze The flow of air from an ocean or lake to the land.

sea-floor spreading The process by which molten material adds new oceanic crust to the ocean floor; occurs along the boundary between diverging plates.

seamount A mountain on the ocean floor that is completely underwater.

secondary color Any color produced by combining equal amounts of any two primary colors.

secondary succession The changes that occur after a disturbance in an ecosystem.

secondary treatment The use of bacteria to break down wastes in wastewater.

secondary wave A transverse seismic wave.

sediment Small, solid pieces of material from rocks or organisms which are moved by water or wind, resulting in erosion and deposition.

sedimentary rock A type of rock that forms when particles from other rocks or the remains of plants and animals are pressed and cemented together.

seed The plant structure that contains a young plant inside a protective covering.

seismic wave A vibration that travels through Earth, carrying the energy released during an earthquake.

seismograph A device that records ground movements caused by seismic waves as they move through Earth; used to detect and measure earthquakes.

selective breeding The process of selecting a few organisms with desired traits to serve as parents of the next generation.

selective cutting The process of cutting down only some trees in an area.

selectively permeable A property of cell membranes that allows some substances to pass through, while others cannot.

semen A mixture of sperm cells and fluids.

semicircular canals Structures in the inner ear that are responsible for the sense of balance.

semiconductor A material that conducts electricity under certain conditions.

Skills and Content Review

sensory neuron A neuron that picks up stimuli from the internal or external environment and converts each stimulus into a nerve impulse.

sepal A leaflike structure that encloses the bud of a flower.

septic tank An underground tank containing bacteria that treat wastewater as it passes through.

series circuit An electric circuit with only one path for the current to take.

sewage Water containing human wastes.

sex-linked gene A gene that is carried on the X or Y chromosome.

sexual reproduction The reproductive process that involves two parents who combine their genetic material to produce a new organism, which differs from both parents.

shareware Software that the author allows others to try out and use for a low fee.

shearing Stress that pushes a mass of rock in opposite directions.

shield volcano A wide, gently sloping mountain made of layers of lava and formed by quiet eruptions.

short circuit An electrical connection that allows current to take an unintended path.

silica A material that is formed from the elements oxygen and silicon; silica is found in magma.

sill A slab of volcanic rock formed when magma squeezes between layers of rock.

skeletal muscle A muscle that is attached to the bones of the skeleton.

sliding friction Friction that occurs when one solid surface slides over another.

slip rings The parts of a generator that rotate with the armature and make contact with the brushes.

slope The steepness, or slant, of a line on a graph.

sludge Deposits of fine solids that settle out from wastewater during the treatment process.

small intestine The part of the digestive system in which most chemical digestion takes place.

smelting The process by which ore is melted to separate the useful metal from other elements.

smooth muscle Involuntary muscle found inside many internal organs of the body.

social health A component of wellness that consists of how well a person gets along with others.

society A group of closely related animals of the same species that work together for the benefit of the whole group.

sod A thick mass of grass roots and soil.

sodium vapor lights Bulbs containing solid sodium plus neon and argon gas that produce light.

soil The loose, weathered material on Earth's surface in which plants can grow.

soil conservation The management of soil to prevent its destruction.

soil horizon A layer of soil that differs in color and texture from the layers above or below it.

solar eclipse The blocking of sunlight to Earth that occurs when the moon is between the sun and Earth.

solar energy Energy from the sun.

solar flare An explosion of hydrogen gas from the sun's surface that occurs when loops in sunspot regions suddenly connect.

solar system A large planetary system that consists of a combination of many smaller planetary systems and objects.

solar wind A stream of electrically charged particles flowing at high speeds from the sun's corona.

solenoid A current-carrying coil of wire with many loops that acts as a magnet.

solid A state of matter that has a definite volume and a definite shape.

solid-state component The part of a circuit in which a signal is controlled by a solid material.

solstice The two days of the year on which the noon sun is directly overhead at either 23.5° south or 23.5° north.

GLOSSARY

Glossary

solubility A measure of how well a solute can dissolve in a solvent at a given temperature.

solute The part of a solution present in a lesser amount and that is dissolved by the solvent.

solution (1) A very well-mixed mixture, having the same properties throughout. (2) A mixture in which one substance is dissolved in another.

solvent The part of a solution that is present in the largest amount and dissolves a solute.

somatic nervous system The group of nerves that controls voluntary actions.

sonar A system that determines the distance of an object under water by recording echoes of sound waves; gets its name from sound navigation and ranging.

sonogram An image formed by an ultrasound machine.

sound A disturbance that travels through a medium as a longitudinal wave.

species A group of similar organisms whose members can mate with one another and produce fertile offspring in nature.

specific heat The amount of thermal energy required to raise the temperature of one kilogram of a substance by one kelvin.

spectrograph An instrument that separates light into colors and photographs the resulting spectrum.

spectroscope An instrument used to view the different colors of light produced by different sources.

spectrum The range of wavelengths of electromagnetic waves.

speed The distance an object travels in one unit of time.

sperm A male sex cell.

sphygmomanometer An instrument that measures blood pressure.

spinal cord The thick column of nerve tissue that is enclosed by the vertebrae and that links the brain to most of the nerves in the peripheral nervous system.

spiral galaxy A galaxy whose arms curve outward in a pinwheel pattern.

spit A beach formed by longshore drift that projects like a finger out into the water.

spontaneous generation The mistaken idea that living things arise from nonliving sources.

spore A tiny cell that is able to grow into a new organism.

sporophyte The stage in the life cycle of a plant in which the plant produces spores for reproduction.

sprain An injury in which the ligaments holding bones together are stretched too far and tear.

spring A place where groundwater bubbles or flows out of cracks in the rocks.

spring tide A tide with the greatest difference between high and low tide that occurs when the sun and the moon are in a line with Earth.

stalactite A calcite deposit that hangs from the roof of a cave.

stalagmite A cone-shaped calcite deposit that builds up from the floor of a cave.

stamen The male reproductive parts of a flower.

standing wave A wave that appears to stand in one place, even though it is really two waves interfering as they pass through each other.

starch A complex carbohydrate in which plants store energy.

states The three forms (solid, liquid, and gas) in which matter exists.

static discharge The loss of static electricity as electric charges move off an object.

static electricity A buildup of charges on an object.

stem The stalk-like organ that supports a plant and that connects the roots to the leaves.

step-down transformer A transformer that decreases voltage.

step-up transformer A transformer that increases voltage.

steppe A prairie or grassland found in the semiarid climate region.

GLOSSARY

Skills and Content Review

stimulant A drug that speeds up body processes.

stimulus A change in an organism's surroundings that causes the organism to react.

stomach A J-shaped, muscular pouch located in the abdomen that expands to hold all of the food that is swallowed.

stomata The small openings on the undersides of most leaves through which oxygen and carbon dioxide can move.

storm A violent disturbance in the atmosphere.

storm surge A dome of water that sweeps across the coast where a hurricane lands.

stratosphere The second-lowest layer of Earth's atmosphere; the ozone layer is located in the upper stratosphere.

stratus Clouds that form in flat layers.

streak The color of a mineral's powder.

stream A channel through which water is continually flowing downhill.

stress (1) A force that acts on rock to change its shape or volume. (2) The reaction of a person's body and mind to threatening, challenging, or disturbing events.

strike-slip fault A type of fault where rocks on either side move past each other sideways with little up-or-down motion.

structure An organism's body plan, or the way its parts are constructed or arranged.

structural formula A description of a molecule that shows the kind, number, and arrangement of atoms.

subarctic A climate zone that lies north of the humid continental climate zone, with short, cool summers and long, bitterly cold winters.

subduction The process by which oceanic crust sinks beneath a deep-ocean trench and back into the mantle at a convergent plate boundary.

sublimation The change in state from a solid directly to a gas without passing through the liquid state.

submersible An underwater vehicle built of strong materials to resist pressure at depth.

subscript A number in a chemical formula that tells the number of atoms in a molecule or the ratio of elements in a compound; written lower and smaller than the symbol.

subsoil The layer of soil beneath the topsoil that contains mostly clay and other minerals.

substance A single kind of matter that has distinct physical and chemical properties.

substituted hydrocarbon A hydrocarbon in which one or more hydrogen atoms have been replaced by atoms of other elements.

succession The series of predictable changes that occur in a community over time.

sunspots Darker, cooler regions on the surface of the sun.

superconductor A material that has no electrical resistance.

supernova The explosion of a dying giant or supergiant star.

supersaturated solution A mixture that has more dissolved solute than is predicted by its solubility at the given temperature.

surface tension The tightness across the surface of water that is caused by the polar molecules pulling on each other.

surface wave (1) A wave that occurs at the surface between two mediums. (2) A type of seismic wave that forms when P waves and S waves reach Earth's surface.

suspension A mixture in which particles can be seen and easily separated by settling or filtration.

sustainable yield A regular amount of a renewable resource that can be harvested without reducing the future supply.

swim bladder An internal gas-filled organ that helps a bony fish stabilize its body at different water depths.

symbiosis A close relationship between two organisms in which at least one of the organisms benefits.

symbol (1) A one- or two-letter set of characters that is used to identify an element. (2) A picture on a map used by mapmakers to stand for a feature on Earth's surface.

GLOSSARY

Glossary

synapse The tiny space between the tip of an axon and the next structure.

syncline A downward fold in rock formed by compression in Earth's crust.

synthesis A chemical reaction in which two or more simple substances combine to form a new, more complex substance.

synthetic A material that is not formed naturally but is manufactured.

T cell A lymphocyte that identifies pathogens and distinguishes one pathogen from the other.

tar A dark, sticky substance produced when tobacco burns.

target cell A cell in the body that recognizes a hormone's chemical structure; a cell to which a hormone binds chemically.

taxol Chemical in yew tree bark that has cancer-fighting properties.

taxonomic key A series of paired statements that describe the physical characteristics of different organisms.

taxonomy The scientific study of how living things are classified.

telescope An optical instrument that forms enlarged images of distant objects.

temperate zones The area between the tropical and polar zones, from about 23.5° to 66.5° north and 23.5° to 66.5° south latitudes.

temperature The average amount of energy of motion in the molecules of a substance.

temperature inversion Condition in which a layer of warm air traps polluted air close to Earth's surface.

tendon A band of connective tissue that attaches a muscle to a bone.

tension Stress that stretches rock so that it becomes thinner in the middle.

terminal The part of an electrode above the surface of the electrolyte.

terminal velocity The maximum velocity a falling object can achieve.

terrestrial planets The name given to the four inner planets: Mercury, Venus, Earth, and Mars.

territory An area that is occupied and defended by an animal or group of animals.

testis Organ of the male reproductive system in which sperm and testosterone are produced.

testosterone A hormone produced by the testes that controls the development of physical characteristics in men.

texture The size, shape, and pattern of a rock's grains.

thermal energy The total energy of a substance's or material's particles due to their movement or vibration.

thermal expansion The expansion of matter when it is heated.

thermogram An image that shows regions of different temperatures in different colors.

thermometer An instrument used to measure temperature, consisting of a thin, glass tube with a bulb on one end that contains a liquid (usually mercury or alcohol).

thermosphere The outermost layer of Earth's atmosphere.

thermostat A device that regulates temperature.

third prong The round prong of a plug which connects the metal shell of an appliance to the safety grounding wire of a building.

thorax An insect's mid-section, to which its wings and legs are attached.

threatened species A species that could become endangered in the near future.

tides The daily rise and fall of Earth's waters on shores.

till The sediments deposited directly by a glacier.

timbre The overall quality of a sound.

tissue A group of similar cells that perform a specific function in an organism.

tolerance A state in which a drug user, after repeatedly taking a drug, needs larger and larger doses of the drug to produce the same effect.

topographic map A map that shows the surface features of an area.

GLOSSARY

topography The shape of the land determined by elevation, relief, and landforms.

topsoil Mixture of humus, clay, and other minerals that forms the crumbly, topmost layer of soil.

tornado A rapidly whirling, funnel-shaped cloud that reaches down from a storm cloud to touch Earth's surface, usually leaving a destructive path.

total internal reflection Complete reflection of light by the inside surface of a medium.

toxic Damaging to the health of humans or other organisms; poisonous.

toxin A poison that can harm an organism.

trace fossils A type of fossil that provides evidence of the activities of ancient organisms.

tracer A radioactive isotope that can be followed through the steps of a chemical reaction or industrial process.

trachea The windpipe; a passage through which air moves in the respiratory system.

trait A characteristic that an organism can pass on to its offspring through its genes.

transfer RNA RNA in the cytoplasm that carries an amino acid to the ribosome and adds it to the growing protein chain.

transform boundary A plate boundary where two plates move past each other in opposite directions.

transformer A device that increases or decreases voltage.

transistor A device that either amplifies an electronic signal or switches current on and off.

transition metal An element in Groups 3 through 12 of the periodic table.

translucent A material that scatters light as it passes through.

transparent A material that transmits light.

transpiration The process by which plants release water vapor through their leaves.

transverse wave A wave that moves the medium in a direction perpendicular to the direction in which the wave travels.

trench A deep canyon in the ocean floor.

trial-and-error learning The learning that occurs when an animal learns to perform a behavior more and more skillfully through repeated practice.

tributary A stream or river that flows into a larger stream or river.

tropical (air mass) A warm air mass that forms in the tropics and has low air pressure.

tropical zone The area near the equator, between about 23.5° north latitude and 23.5° south latitude.

tropism The growth response of a plant toward or away from a stimulus.

troposphere The lowest layer of Earth's atmosphere, where weather occurs.

trough The lowest point of a transverse wave.

tsunami A large surface wave on the ocean caused by an earthquake on the ocean floor.

tumor A mass of abnormal cells that develops when cancerous cells divide and grow uncontrollably.

tundra A polar climate region, found across northern Alaska, Canada, and Russia, with short, cool summers and bitterly cold winters, or a similar extremely cold, dry biome.

tungsten-halogen lights Bulbs containing a tungsten filament and a halogen gas that produce light.

turbine A circular device with many blades that is turned by water, wind, steam, or tides.

turbulence A type of movement of water in which, rather than moving downstream, the water moves every which way.

ultrasound Sound waves with frequencies above 20,000 Hz.

ultraviolet radiation A form of energy with wavelengths that are shorter than visible light.

ultraviolet rays Electromagnetic waves with frequencies higher than visible light, but lower than X-rays.

© Pearson Education, Inc.

GLOSSARY

umbilical cord A ropelike structure that forms in the uterus between the embryo and the placenta.

umbra The darkest part of a shadow.

unbalanced force A nonzero net force that changes an object's motion.

unconformity A place where an old, eroded surface is in contact with a newer rock layer.

understory A layer of shorter plants that grow in the shade of a forest canopy.

unicellular A type of organism that is made up of a single cell.

universe All of space and everything in it.

unsaturated fats Fats, such as olive oil and canola oil, that are usually liquid at room temperature.

unsaturated hydrocarbon A hydrocarbon in which one or more of the bonds between carbon atoms is double or triple.

unsaturated solution A mixture in which more solute can be dissolved.

unsaturated zone A layer of rocks and soil above the water table in which the pores contain air as well as water.

upwelling An upward flow of cold water from the ocean depths.

urea A chemical that comes from the breakdown of proteins and is removed from the body by the kidneys.

ureter A narrow tube that carries urine from one of the kidneys to the urinary bladder.

urethra A small tube through which urine flows from the body.

urinary bladder A sacklike muscular organ that stores urine until it is eliminated from the body.

urine A watery fluid produced by the kidneys that contains urea and other waste materials.

uterus The hollow muscular organ of the female reproductive system in which a baby develops.

vaccination The process by which harmless antigens are deliberately introduced into a person's body to produce active immunity.

vaccine A substance used in a vaccination that consists of pathogens that have been weakened or killed but can still trigger the immune system into action.

vacuole A water-filled sac inside a cell that acts as a storage area.

vacuum tube A glass tube from which almost all gases have been removed, and which contains electrodes that control the flow of electrons.

vagina A muscular passageway through which a baby leaves the mother's body.

valence electrons The electrons that are farthest away from the nucleus of an atom and are involved in chemical reactions.

valley glacier A long, narrow glacier that forms when snow and ice build up in mountain valleys.

valve A flap of tissue in the heart or a vein that prevents blood from flowing backward.

Van Allen belts Two doughnut-shaped regions 1,000–25,000 kilometers above Earth that contain electrons and protons traveling at high speeds.

vaporization The change from the liquid to the gaseous form, or state, of matter.

variable Any factor that can change in an experiment.

variation Any difference between individuals of the same species.

vary inversely A term used to describe the relationship between two variables whose graph forms a curve that slopes downward from left to right.

vascular plant A plant that has vascular tissue.

vascular tissue The internal transporting tissue in some plants that is made up of tubelike structures.

vein (1) A blood vessel that carries blood back to the heart. (2) A narrow slab of a mineral that is sharply different from the surrounding rock.

velocity Speed in a given direction.

vent The opening through which molten rock and gas leave a volcano.

GLOSSARY

ventricle The lower chamber of the heart, which pumps blood out to the lungs and body.

vernal equinox The day of the year that marks the beginning of spring in the Northern Hemisphere.

vertebrae The bones that make up the backbone of a vertebrate.

vertebrate An animal that has a backbone.

vibration A repeated back-and-forth or up-and-down motion.

villi Tiny finger-shaped structures that cover the inner surface of the small intestine and provide a large surface area through which digested food is absorbed.

villus One of the tiny finger-shaped structures that cover the inner surface of the small intestine and provide a large surface area through which digested food is absorbed.

virtual image An upright image formed where rays of light appear to meet or come from.

virus A small, nonliving particle that invades and then reproduces inside a living cell.

viscosity The resistance of a liquid to flowing.

visible light Electromagnetic radiation that can be seen with the unaided eye.

vitamin An organic compound that serves as a helper molecule in a variety of chemical reactions in the body.

vocal cords Folds of connective tissue that stretch across the opening of the larynx and produce a person's voice.

volcanic neck A deposit of hardened magma in a volcano's pipe.

volcano A weak spot in the crust where magma comes to the surface.

voltage The difference in electrical potential between two places.

voltage source A device, such as a battery or generator, that creates a potential difference in an electric circuit.

voltmeter A device used to measure voltage, or potential difference.

volume The amount of space that matter occupies.

voluntary muscle A muscle that is under conscious control.

water cycle The continuous process by which water moves from Earth's surface and to the atmosphere and back, passing through the living and nonliving parts of the environment.

water pollution The addition of any substance that has a negative effect on water or on the living things that depend on the water.

water quality The degree of purity of water, determined by measuring the substances in water, besides water molecules.

water table The top of the saturated zone, or depth to the groundwater in an aquifer.

water vapor The invisible, gaseous form of water.

water vascular system A system of fluid-filled tubes in an echinoderm's body.

watershed The land area that supplies water to a river system.

wave A disturbance that transfers energy from place to place, for example, through a body of water.

wave height The vertical distance from the crest of a wave to the trough.

wavelength The distance between the crest of one wave and the crest of the next.

weather The condition of Earth's atmosphere at a particular time and place.

weathering The chemical and physical processes that break down rock at Earth's surface.

wedge A simple machine consisting of a device that is thick at one end and tapers to a thin edge at the other.

weight A measure of the force of gravity on an object.

wellness The state of being at the best possible level of health—in the body, the mind, and relationships with others.

Glossary

wet cell An electrochemical cell in which the electrolyte is a liquid.

wetland An area of land that is covered with a shallow layer of water during some or all of the year.

wheel and axle A simple machine consisting of two circular or cylindrical objects that are fastened together and rotate about a common axis.

white blood cell A blood cell that fights disease.

white dwarf The remaining hot core of a star after its outer layers have expanded and drifted out into space.

wide area network (WAN) A system of computers connected across large distances.

wind The horizontal movement of air from an area of high pressure to an area of lower pressure.

wind-chill factor Increased cooling caused by the wind.

windward The side of mountains that faces the oncoming wind.

withdrawal A period of adjustment that occurs when a drug-dependent person stops taking the drug.

work The product of force and distance when a force is used to move an object.

World Wide Web A system that allows the displaying of text, pictures, video, and sound on the Internet.

X-ray Electromagnetic waves with higher frequencies than ultraviolet rays, but shorter than gamma rays.

xylem The vascular tissue through which water and nutrients move in some plants.

zygote A fertilized egg, produced by the joining of a sperm and an egg.

Skills and Content Review

GLOSSARY